MACHINES, MILLS AND UNCOUNTABLE COSTLY NECESSITIES

A short history of the drainage of the fens

MACHINES
MILLS
AND UNCOUNTABLE
COSTLY NECESSITIES

A short history of the drainage of the fens

Richard L. Hills M.A.

GOOSE & SON
PUBLISHERS, NORWICH
1967

PLAQUE ON THE HUNDRED FOOT ENGINE, 1830

These Fens *have oft times been by* Water *drown'd*
Science a remedy in Water *found*
The power of Steam *she said shall be employ'd*
And the Destroyer *by* Itself *destroy'd.*

PLAQUE ON THE BURNT FEN ENGINE, 1842

In fitness for the urgent hour,
Unlimited, untiring power,
Precision, promptitude, command
The infant's will the giant's hand;
Steam, mighty Steam ascends the throne,
and reigns lord paramount alone.

Printed by Lithography in Great Britain
by Jarrold and Sons Ltd, Norwich

Contents

List of Abbreviations

List of Illustrations

List of Illustrations continued

Preface

It would be impossible to thank individually the many people who have given assistance in forwarding this work, and so I ask that those who are not mentioned here will accept my deep appreciation of their help and kindness towards me. However, I would like to thank Dr J. P. C. Roach, then at Corpus Christi College, Cambridge, who gave encouragement in the initial stages, and introduced me to Archer and Archer of Ely where Colonel J. A. G. Beckett made available the records of the Waterbeach Level. Other Clerks to Fen Drainage Boards have given great assistance, including Hall Ennion and Young, also of Ely, Mr R. J. Brooks, Clerk to the Littleport and Downham Board, and Mr Swann of the North Level and Thorney Internal Drainage Board.

The County Record Offices of Cambridge and Lincoln have delved into their innermost recesses to find some of their records, and other librarians, especially at the Institution of Civil Engineers and at the Birmingham Public Library, have been equally sympathetic and helpful. The comparison of developments in the English Fens with similar Dutch problems was made possible through the generosity of the Shell Company who enabled me to study the drainage works in Holland.

Even with all this help, the work would have been impossible without the aid of Messrs E. J. A. Kenny and R. H. Clark, who have provided many of the photographs and given aid in other ways. I must also acknowledge my debt to Mr C. O. Clarke, Superintendent of the Waterbeach Level, who has given me so much invaluable information through his experience of fen drainage while his wife has provided excellent gingerbread and tea. Finally, without the advice of Professor and Mrs A. R. Hall, this book would never have progressed beyond vague ideas, and it is only through them that this work has made its appearance.

CHAPTER I

The Sink of Thirteen Counties

The villages of Stretham and Wicken are not the most spectacular places to begin an investigation of fenland drainage, for in this part of the Fens there are no large fortifications against floods nor have there been any dramatic cases of the banks bursting and water pouring over the land. For centuries men have laboured to win this land from its original waste and desolate state and their unremitting struggle has been carried on almost without notice, but in this area six miles south of Ely there is a wealth of historical features that in themselves tell the story of man's fight against the floods. Between Wicken village and the River Cam lies the only part of the Fens that still resembles the original state of this whole area. Wicken Fen, now preserved by the National Trust, remains covered with marsh and reed and peaty turf which quakes and trembles as you walk over it. Here some varieties of plants which need plenty of water for their existence are carefully cherished, since elsewhere they have almost died out. This is also a place of refuge for birds whose habitat is marsh land or water, for the rest of the Fens have been drained and turned into agricultural land.

Stretham parish has some land in the Waterbeach Level District which is the southernmost part of the Fens. From the village of Waterbeach, which is about six miles north of Cambridge, it is over forty miles to the sea at King's Lynn and it is over seventy miles to the most northerly fen district which is by the River Witham close to Lincoln. From east to west the Fens stretch from Brandon in Suffolk to Peterborough (about thirty-six miles) and from King's Lynn to a little east of Stamford (about thirty-four miles).[1] The fenland itself covers an area of 1,306 square miles, but the catchment area which drains through this basin is nearly 6,000 square miles in extent. The rivers that flow through the Fens drain a large part of the centre of England and as Defoe says, "All the Water, or most part of the Water of thirteen Counties, falls into them."[2]

The main river of this basin, the Great Ouse, used to flow close to Stretham but this part of the river, now called the Old West, was by-passed in the first great undertaking to drain the Fens in the middle of the seventeenth century. The Ouse rises beyond Brackley in Northamptonshire and wanders eastwards and northwards to the sea at King's Lynn. Five tributaries, the Cam or Granta, the Lark, the Little Ouse, the Wissey and the Nar, flow from the chalk uplands which border the Fens on their eastern side and join the Ouse before it reaches the sea. Four other rivers, the Nene, the Welland, the Glen and the Witham, rise in the sandstone ridges of Lincoln and Northamptonshire and flow through the Fens in their western half. Between the highlands of chalk on one side and sandstone on the other, lies a bed of clay. On top of it are occasional outcrops of green sandstone which have formed islands such as the Isle of Ely, but the basic stratum under the Fens is either Oxford or Kimmeridge Clay. It is highest towards the south from where it slopes gently down until it is well below sea-level under the Wash. No water can soak through it so that any rain which falls upon it or any water which comes from the higher land around this clay basin has to lie on top until the rivers can carry the water to the sea.

In times of heavy rain the rivers are unable to cope with the volume of water that pours into the Fens from the higher catchment area. As Daniel Defoe on his tour through Great

1

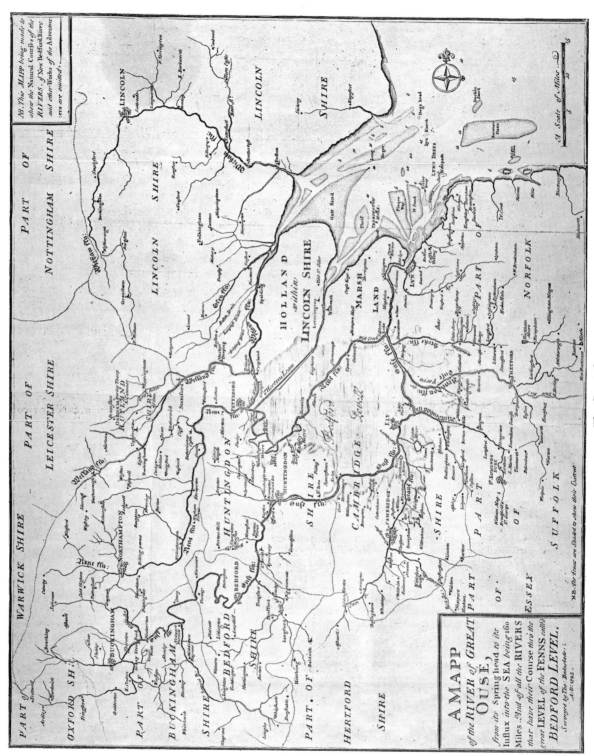

The Great Ouse

2

The windmill from Adventurer's Fen now preserved in Wicken Fen

Britain crossed the Gogmagog Hills towards Cambridge, he saw the "Fen country almost all covered with water like a sea: the Michaelmas Rains having been very great that Year, they had sent great floods of Water from the Upland Countries, and these Fenns being as may be very properly said, the sink of no less than thirteen Counties . . . they are often overflowed."[3] The fenman has always striven to remove the water from his land, whether it came by rain or flood, and his ability to do this has ultimately depended upon the success of the rivers carrying away their contents to the sea. In the pages that follow, we shall be considering principally the way people have tried to keep their own lands free from floods, but to understand this it is also necessary to see how the rivers have coped with their burden.

The individual farmer, or group of owners of a small area, could build a bank round the land, but after a time this did not prove enough. In fact, the great scheme which turned the Old West into its present insignificance and shortened the Great Ouse by some twelve miles, also showed that it was necessary to have some means whereby the water on the land could be lifted from the drain-level to the rivers. This led to the general introduction of the windmill and in Wicken Fen is preserved the last windmill that pumped water out of a fen for drainage purposes. This mill was originally built in the near-by Adventurers Fen, but it was moved to its present site in order to preserve it. Now it is sometimes used to pump water into the fen to prevent the peat-bog drying out, for the land all round has shrunk and disappeared through drainage and is now much lower than Wicken Fen itself. During the beginning of the nineteenth century, improvements to the rivers did not result in a

3

natural drainage and the farmers found that windmills could not drain their land adequately. They began to employ steam-engines for this purpose and one of these, the Stretham engine, is preserved three miles north-west of Wicken Fen. It was built in 1831 to drain the Waterbeach Level and is typical of the first steam-engines used in the Fens. The tall chimney was once a common feature, pouring out smoke over the fields, but now the steam-engine has followed the windmill into oblivion. None of these changes happened suddenly, for the Fens cover a very large area, and traditional ways die hard in these parts. Even when steam-engines were being replaced by diesels after the First World War, one or two windmills still remained at work.

All of these engines are useless when the floods rise so high that they can no longer pump. The individual farmer living in the Waterbeach Level forty miles from the sea depends upon the efficient functioning of the river outfalls for the preservation of his land. The Old West is only a few feet higher than low tide level in the Wash, and some of the Waterbeach Level drains are lower than the lowest level the sea reaches. As the rivers flow through this flat land, they lose their speed, and by the time they reach the sea, they have left very little scouring power to keep their channels clear. A certain amount of silt is brought down especially by floods,[4] and it used to be assumed that this was a serious problem. However, silt samplings taken by the River Great Ouse Catchment Board from 1937 to 1939 show that silt from this source is negligible in quantity. It is the "ill disposition of the Sea in those parts, which being troubled by stormy windes, doe carry such abundance of Silt or Sand into the Outfalls".[5] In fact, the sea brings so much silt into the Wash that mud-flats are being continually built up and then reclaimed for cultivation. At the present time, about half of the Fens consist of silt land deposited by the sea and this area is gradually being extended.

Nevertheless, the rivers do determine the place where the silt is deposited, and the positions of the mud-banks and sand-bars at their mouths depend upon the relative strength of tide and river.

Thus if the seasons are wet, the Rivers having a greater quantity of water in them, run to seaward with a greater velocity, and of consequence drive the silt further out; on the other hand, if the seasons are dry, and the tides stronger than the effects of wind or other causes, the silt of course is driven less powerfully outwards, and settles nearer to their mouths which choaks them up, and prevents their free discharge from the Fens.[6]

During a dry summer there was not enough water flowing down to keep the river-mouths clear so that the channels became blocked and were not large enough to carry away the first floods of winter. These floods had to clear their own passage through the silt-banks to the sea, but before they could do this, the water rose in the rivers, threatening the safety of the banks. Not only was the countryman in danger of utter ruin, but the navigation down the rivers to the ports was seriously disrupted.[7] In some years it was a long time before the silt-banks were washed away, and winter might be almost over before the obstructions were removed and a clear passage gained. Of course the drier the summer, the more the rivers were filled and choked with sand and silt, and if a wet winter followed, then there was a danger that there might be great inundations.[8]

These silt lands remained subject to flooding by the sea until people built banks to keep the tides out. A normal high tide rises about 18 feet above low water, but strong winds and floods may make it rise a further 6 feet. In places the silt areas had built up until they lay above high spring tide, or about 20 feet above low water, but in general in those parts where the towns and villages were built, the land varied from 15 to 17 feet above normal low water, and in other parts about 10 feet above low tide level.[9] Once this area had been

The Great LEVEL . . . as it lay drowned

properly embanked, most of this land was close enough to the sea to have a natural drainage provided that the outfalls were cleared and the rivers kept free from silt and floods.

Farther to the south, behind the silt-banks, another type of land was literally growing up. Before any attempts had been made at drainage, the blocking of the outfalls meant that the flood water flowed over the land and made it a freshwater lake. This gave ideal conditions for marshes to grow and develop into huge beds of peat, many feet thick. These marshes themselves helped to block up the rivers and it is possible to see winding across the fen fields many old river courses or "roddens" which have been abandoned when the river cut a new channel. The peat continued to grow until the general level of this area was higher than the silt lands. To the drainage speculators of the sixteenth and seventeenth centuries, it appeared that these peat-marshes would be as easy to drain as the silt land. In 1589 Humphrey Bradley from Bergen-op-Zoom in Flanders drew up a scheme for draining the Fens and submitted it to Lord Burghley. It was rejected, perhaps because English pride would not allow a foreigner to do the work, although Bradley was of English descent,[10] but this treatise does show the difference in levels between the peat and silt lands. In his survey, Bradley pointed out that

practically the entire surface of the land is above high sea-level, and the lowest part of all (very small) is at least six or seven feet above low sea-level. So that, to free it [i.e. the land] means nothing else than draining the superfluity of waters, from the uplands to the lowlands, and from above to below, as there is a slope of sixteen to seventeen feet through which the sea rises and falls from high to low tide; and yet the enterprise does not need anything but some assistance given to nature, by which the waters can be led through channels of convenient depth and width, to the outlets, that are at hand, particularly the rivers of Lynn and Boston, there to empty themselves into the sea.

The greater part of South Holland and Marshland and many other places, lying lower than the inundated lands by six or seven feet and separated from the Marsh only by embankments, remain dry. So if the outlets suffice to drain the water from the low flats, should we be doubtful of that from the high ground?[11]

This was still true sixty years later, for Dodson writing in 1665 agreed that the peat lands were higher than the silt lands,[12] and all these early writers concluded that the Fens were high enough to drain themselves, provided that the rivers were made adequate.

The cause of the swamping of the Fens was thought to lie in the choking of the rivers. These and all the smaller ditches which ought to have carried the water to the sea "had become totally fordable, and in many places even two or three feet higher than the greater part of the land to be drained".[13] It seemed that all that was needed was the deepening of the rivers and so Bradley and other Dutchmen came to England with high hopes for they thought that the Fens had many advantages over their own country where

many water-works are undertaken and completed subject to ten times as great difficulty for the sake of some little plot of ground not (as to the thousandth part) of the size and benefit of this, and where it is needful to have recourse to means – dikes, machines, mills and uncountable costly necessities – because the lands lie beneath the low tide or a little above it: these marshes [the Fens] have all the advantages and helps that Nature can give, above those of Holland.[14]

However, the drainage of the Fens was not so simple as this because both peat and silt land contracts as it is properly drained. The silt land, now that it is dry, has dropped 2 or 3 feet,[15] while the peat has shrunk much more. Ditches and dikes cut through the peat become too shallow after a few years to drain the land. Some people thought that the bottoms of the ditches grew up, but Dodson suggested that it was the neighbouring ground

A gang "slubbing", or cleaning the outfall drain of the Upware engine which can be seen in the background (C.O.C.)

that sank and became firmer.[16] He thought that the ditches would be maintained if they were dug out again after the initial shrinkage had taken place, and this would be so, but only if the surrounding water-level was not lowered at the same time. If the water-level were lowered, then the whole process would start all over again for neither Bradley nor Dodson, nor for another 200 years did anyone fully realize the nature of peat.

It was well known that there was no solidity in peat, for banks made with it looked firm and solid, but in four or five years shrank to half their former size.[17] These "hollow counterfeit banks, made of so light a composition that it will both burn and swim"[18] rotted away to a mould and were useless against a winter flood[19] because peat is composed almost entirely of vegetable matter that is eaten by bacteria when it is dry. In course of time, the peat will completely vanish, for the process of drying and disappearing will go on until the clay substratum is reached. The early drainers could not know this, but it took a very long time before the extent of the shrinkage and wastage was realized. This explains why gravitation schemes for drainage could be suggested for so many years, for even as late as 1809 John Rennie believed that the Fens would drain themselves without pumping machinery.[20] Yet by 1830 this view had almost died out,[21] although the part played by bacteria was not realized until some years later. Wheeler believed that the Fens in Rennie's day were about 4 feet higher than in 1890 when he was writing,[22] and this shrinkage is still continuing on the peat lands. Better drainage, especially since the introduction of the steam-engine, has hastened this process because the water-level can be properly controlled and does not depend on the strength of the wind.

A further factor, which has caused many of the problems in the Fens but which only now is beginning to be investigated, is the gradual subsidence of the whole area. Calculations based on excavations in the Norfolk Broads suggest that there may have been a short period before A.D. 800 when the land was rising, but since then there has been a steady fall tending to become less the nearer we approach our present time. This might be between $\frac{3}{4}$ and 1 inch in every ten years,[23] and if it has been taking place over a good many centuries, it will help to explain why the deposits of peat and silt are so deep. Excavations and aerial photographs of the Fens show that the Romans cultivated and inhabited parts which today can be kept free from drowning only by extensive banking and drainage works. Conditions must have deteriorated soon after they left, for monks and hermits were attracted by the desolation and emptiness of the area.

During the Middle Ages, great stretches of fen were owned by abbeys and monasteries, for example Chatteris, Crowland, Denny, Ely, Peterborough, Ramsey and Thorney. The monks supervised some primitive forms of drainage, for they derived much of their income from the Fens, and the fenmen themselves were continually trying to win portions which they might use for pasture or even arable,[24] but there was never any extensive project of reclamation and the monasteries did little more than maintain the banks of the existing river courses. When the lands passed into private ownership at the Dissolution of the Monasteries, there was a certain amount of confusion and lack of attention from the new owners, but there is little to show that an intelligent and co-ordinated drainage system was destroyed.[25] In the same way as they had punished and fined the abbots, the Courts of Sewers continued to charge the new owners for neglecting to maintain their banks and ditches.[26] Yet one result was a greater number of small and often conflicting interests which made it harder to initiate any comprehensive drainage scheme, while, with the growing wealth of England in Tudor times and new ideas and inventions coming from the Continent, the demand for better drainage increased because good years showed people the potential value of fenland.

It is difficult to draw any accurate picture of agriculture in the Fens during the sixteenth and seventeenth centuries because conditions varied so much from year to year. Sometimes rain and snow would cause the rivers to rise and flood the land as happened in 1947, while in another year an easterly storm coinciding with a high spring tide would pile the waters up in the Wash until the sea poured over the banks as in 1953.

It is a hard question, whether the Sea or the Land floods are the most potent enemies to the Fenns; but this is most certaine, that when the Sea floods and the Land floods meet, as they often times doe, halfe way betwixt the high Lands and the Sea, in that very place like two powerful enimies joyning in one, they doe over-run the Levell, and drowne it from one end unto the other.[27]

It was quite common for most of the Fens to be under water during a large part of the winter, but Casaubon, a scholar from the Continent who visited the Fens in 1611, pointed out that these floods did not enrich the land as in Egypt, for these areas were useless for anything else except grazing.[28] Some parts like that between Downham and Wisbech he found resembled a marsh "where nothing grows except reeds",[29] and it was in such an area that he saw a man on stilts driving 400 cows to pasture with the help of only a little boy. Those areas that remained dry all winter supported a large stock of cattle and even sheep. If the winter were moderate and the spring dry so that the water had a chance to run off the land, the flocks and herds would be driven into the lower parts of the Fens.[30] The farmers realized that, if they could secure an adequate drainage, they could use these lower areas for the whole of the year with great benefit to themselves.

There was the example of Holland just across the sea where large drainage works had been undertaken with great success,[31] and it was considered a national disgrace to have this large useless area stretching into the heart of England. During the wars at the end of

Queen Elizabeth's reign many Englishmen went to Holland and fought against Spain. Fenmen went too, for the Privy Council asked that a dozen of the best able and most expert stiltmen from the Lincolnshire Fens to be "furnished . . . with two pairs of the highest stiltes at the least and the longest poles"[32] and sent to the Earl of Leicester in the Low Countries. These people would have seen the drainage works in Holland and realized the possibilities in the Fens. Dutchmen also came to England; some seeking refuge from the invading Spanish armies only wanted somewhere to live in safety and a few settled near Thorney where they drained part of that area.[33] Others came to England because they realized they might make their fortunes out of drainage schemes here. Such a one was Humphrey Bradley, but there were others with lesser ideas, like Peter Morrice and William Mostart, who tried to obtain patents for machines or engines "to draw waters above their natural Levill"[34] and drain fens and low grounds.

The fenmen were interested in using these machines because there seems to have been a worsening in conditions towards the end of the sixteenth century. These were years of bad harvest for the rest of the country through excessive rainfall. Not only were the fen people hit by the high prices of corn, but they were swamped by floods from the highlands. In their distress they appealed for help to the Privy Council in 1596, because they had sustained great loss

by the outragious innundations and overflowinge of waters descendinge from the higher parts . . . in so muche that a great number of the said inhabitants of those countis togeather with their families are verie greatly impoverished and like to be overthrowne and utterly undone, to the great hinderance of the State, yf som spedy remedy be not had and provided.[35]

In November 1598 there were further bad floods throughout the Fens,[36] which caused greater distress following so soon on top of the others. Many farmers were in dire trouble and could hardly continue for besides the general scarcity of all corn and other provisions, there had been many continuously wet years, and through the great inundations, they had lost many cattle which they were unable to recover by breeding.[37]

The individual farmer was always liable to find himself in such a plight because he had no control over the rivers, and so small groups of villagers who held common rights over parts of the Fens had to take what measures they could to protect their land against the ravages of rain and floods. Any large-scale work in the Fens necessitated an Act of Parliament to provide adequate safeguards for those whose land would be drained and for those who adventured the money. Delays occurred while the fenlanders argued over the merits of various schemes, and when a plan had been agreed, a process which often took many years, there were still the delays of Parliamentary proceedings and raising the finances afterwards.

There were two main schools of thought which put forward conflicting suggestions. There were those who thought it required only a thorough cleansing and embanking of the rivers to once more secure the Fens in their former pristine condition. The works that the Almighty had made would obviously be best in their natural places. If the rivers were restored to their preordained places, and deepened and contained between proper banks, they would flow with greater velocity to the sea and take the floods away more quickly.[38] The greatest proponent of these ideas was the Dutchman Jan Barents Westerdyke. His original plans for draining the whole of the Fens were defeated in 1630 by another Dutchman, his great rival Vermuyden. In 1649 he was again asked to suggest alternatives to Vermuyden's plans, but Vermuyden triumphed a second time.[39]

The other school of thought considered that the Almighty needed a helping hand to ensure that the outfalls of the rivers were kept clear. To obtain an adequate scour, either

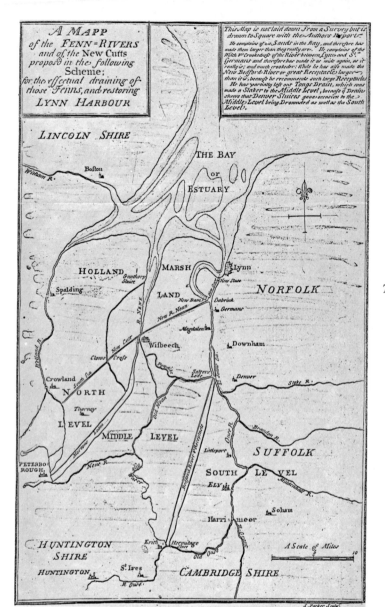

A MAPP
of the FENN=RIVERS
and of the New Cutts
propos'd in the following
Scheme;
for the effectual draining of
those Fenns, and restoring
LYNN HARBOUR

The Fen rivers

the quantity of water had to be increased, or the same volume of water had to be accelerated to give it greater force. Following the former of these two ideas, William Dodson suggested combining the fenland rivers in one outfall, for he thought that one large river would have an adequate scour as there would be more water running regularly all the year. He may have put forward this scheme in 1649 when he was Director of the Bedford Level and he suggested it again in 1665, these being times when Vermuyden's schemes were not fulfilling their early promise. Dodson had been employed on Vermuyden's first drainage works in 1630, and during the Civil War he was appointed Governor of Crowland, so he had considerable experience of fenland drainage.[40] Taking his example from Holland where the tides were shut out from the rivers by sluices, he proposed building a substantial sluice near St Germans to prevent the tides silting the rivers. Not only did he intend to make the Ouse run out through this sluice but also the River Nene, which he planned to divert in a new channel from Wisbech

by sufficient banks of good sollid Earth; then have I sufficient waterway for all those Freshes to the Sea, which will force good Navigation, and maintain the Chennel Winter, and Summer, to the great benefit of all those Sea men which use that Port of Lynne; and all the Rivers in and out of the Level will be bettered, and improved.[41]

This scheme of Dodson's may have had some influence on the building of Denver Sluice on the Ouse, but nothing has ever been done to combine the rivers.

All improvements before and since have relied on the principle of straightening the rivers in order to shorten the distance to the sea and thereby increase the fall per mile. Bishop Morton was the first to do this in about 1490 when he straightened the Nene from Stanground near Peterborough to Guyhirne, six miles up-stream from Wisbech. This cut, 12 miles long, 40 feet wide and 4 feet deep, was a large undertaking for the end of the fifteenth century, and set the example for others to follow.[42] In 1609 another part of the Nene was straightened under the direction of Lord Chief Justice Popham,[43] and similar ideas formed the basis of the only plan from 1630 to modern times for draining the whole of the Fens.

The man behind the plan of 1630 was Cornelius Vermuyden who had come to England around 1620 because he hoped to participate in the schemes that were being suggested for draining the Fens. Nothing happened, so he went farther north and drained Hatfield Chase in 1626. Then a group of Adventurers, headed by the fourth Earl of Bedford, secured a Royal Order to drain the Fens. There was no Parliament from which they could obtain an Act, so the Order was based on earlier Acts passed under Henry VIII and Elizabeth.[44] Vermuyden designed a series of cuts to straighten the rivers and keep most of the flood water out of the Fens. The most famous work undertaken at this time was the Bedford River from Earith to Denver which by-passed the old twisting course of the Ouse by Stretham and Ely. Not all of Vermuyden's plans were carried out because he met with fierce opposition from the fenmen who destroyed his banks and ditches. The Civil War intervened, money ran short, and Vermuyden found himself at the centre of bitter arguments during the next thirty years. The rivers still did not have sufficient scour in summer to keep the channels clear. In some wet years, the outfalls would be good, but bitter experience had taught the fenmen not to trust that they would always remain in that state,[45] and more flooding proved them right.

NOTES

1. S. H. Miller, *A Handbook to the Fenland* (1889), intro., p. iii.
2. D. Defoe, *A Tour through the whole Island of Great Britain* (1724), vol. I, p. 114.
3. ibid.
4. J. Rennie, Report on Wildmore Fens, 7 April 1800, p. 349.
5. A. Burrell, *A Briefe Relation . . .* (1642), p. 5.
6. J. Rennie, loc. cit.
7. W. Dodson, *The Designe . . .* (1665), p. 5.
8. W. Elstobb, *Some Thoughts on Rosewell's and other Schemes . . .* (1742), p. 4.
9. W. H. Wheeler, *The History of the Fens of South Lincolnshire* (1897), p. 1, and Fen Tracts, *Observations on the means of better draining the South Levels of the Fens by two gentlemen . . .* (1777).
10. L. E. Harris, *Vermuyden and the Fens* (1953), p. 27.
11. H. Bradley, for the original in Italian see Lansdowne, 60/34, but most is translated in H. C. Darby, *The Draining of the Fens* (1940), p. 262.
12. W. Dodson, op. cit., p. 4.
13. A. Burrell, op. cit., pp. 3–4.
14. H. Bradley, cf. H. C. Darby, op. cit., p. 261.
15. H. C. Darby, op. cit., p. 108.
16. W. Dodson, op. cit., p. 17.

17. A. Burrell, *Exceptions against Sir Cornelius Vermuyden's Discourse* . . . (1642), p. 11.
18. A. Burrell, *A Briefe Relation* . . . (1642), intro.
19. W. Dodson, op. cit., p. 14, and A. Burrell, *Exceptions* . . . (1642), p. 11.
20. J. Rennie, Report and Estimate . . . of the South and Middle Levels. . . , 24 May 1809.
21. S. Wells, *The History of the Drainage of the Great Level of the Fens, called Bedford Level* (1830), vol. I, p. 439.
22. W. H. Wheeler, *Report on the Improvement of the River Ouse* . . . (1884), p. 8.
23. J. M. Lambert, *The Making of the Broads*, R.G.S. Series (1960).
24. H. C. Darby, *The Medieval Fenland* (1940), p. 51.
25. L. E. Harris, op. cit., p. 53.
26. See Bedford Level Corporation, Records of Earlier Courts of Sewers.
27. A. Burrell, *A Briefe Relation* . . . (1642), p. 5.
28. I. Casaubon, *Ephemerides* (1611), vol. II, p. 869.
29. ibid., p. 871.
30. W. Blith, *The English Improver Improved* (2nd ed. 1652), p. 50.
31. W. Dodson, op. cit., p. 23.
32. Acts of the Privy Council, 24 April 1586, p. 75.
33. Lansdowne MS., 110/5, p. 22.
34. S.P., Dom. Eliz., 106/62.
35. Acts of the Privy Council, 2 March 1596, p. 537.
36. ibid., 5 November 1598, p. 264.
37. Lansdowne MS., 87/4, p. 11.
38. L. E. Harris, op. cit., p. 96.
39. ibid., pp. 66 and 94.
40. ibid., p. 96.
41. W. Dodson, op. cit., p. 7.
42. H. C. Darby, *The Medieval Fenland* (1940), p. 167, and L. E. Harris, op. cit., p. 18.
43. H. C. Darby, *The Draining of the Fens* (1940), p. 31, and L. E. Harris, op. cit., p. 27.
44. 23 Hen. VIII, c. 5, and 43 Eliz. I, c. 11.
45. W. Dodson, op. cit., p. 4.

CHAPTER II

Machines, Mills and Uncountable Costly Necessities

The farmer could throw a bank round his land to keep out the flood waters, but in many places the land was not high enough to drain naturally into the rivers. If the river-levels could not be lowered, the farmers had to use some machine to pump the water off the land into the rivers. In the late Middle Ages the sources of power were the muscles of man and beast or the force of the wind, for the rivers did not have sufficient fall in the Fens for water power to be utilized. Scoops or ladles were used by men, but the most obvious source of power was the windmill which alone could provide enough energy to clear a large area of water. The adaptation of the windmill from grinding corn to raising water was first accomplished in Holland, and a document of the reign of Count William IV (1344) mentions the sale of corn-mills and wind-driven water-mills (marsh-mills) in Drechterland.[1] References to mills "throwing water" occur more frequently in Dutch manuscripts as the fifteenth century progresses, so some could have been built in the Fens as early as that.

Monasteries would have had the resources and organization to build mills, and there are references to mills (*molendina*) in several documents but there is nothing to show whether these were mills worked by wind or water for grinding corn, or driven by wind to raise water. There are some records of Courts of Sewers where the term "mill" would seem to indicate a windmill, but whether to grind corn or pump water cannot be determined. For example, there was a Court of Sewers held in 1395 when it was decided

that the Towne of Spalding ought to repayre and heighten the said banks in Spalding next Welland water . . . from the Abbots mill [of Crowland] unto Spalding Drove . . . and that Thomas the Abbot of Croiland and the Convent of the same place and their ought to repair the same bank next Welland water from the said messuage of Wm. Kellod unto Dole mill dike.[2]

At the Dissolution of the Monasteries, various "molenda" are mentioned in the monastic estates. Some of these are definitely water-driven mills, for example, that of Chatteris Abbey at Hemingford Grey,[3] but there was also a "molendum" at Thorney and one at Ramsey,[4] where there is very little fall in the rivers for driving water-mills.

One difficulty is to know what term would have been used to describe a windmill that pumped water. "Engine" is the English term used during the late sixteenth century and in official documents it was retained until well into the eighteenth century.[5] Yet by the beginning of the seventeenth century, the words "engine" and "mill" were interchangeable and used to describe a water-raising windmill.[6] If "windmill" were used in common parlance long before this to describe a water-raising machine, then a windmill shown on Hayward's Map of the Great Level, 1604, near Fosdike on the sea-bank might be the windmill mentioned by the Commissioners of Sewers in the parts of Holland (Lincolnshire) in 1555. They complained that "the see [bank] bilongyng to Algerkyrk and Fosdyk from the wyndemill unto Cromer Hyrn is in decay".[7] An inspection of the site has revealed remains of a windmill beside the old sea-bank with two ditches leading up to it, so it was obviously used to pump water.

The more settled conditions during the reign of Queen Elizabeth prompted various people to try and obtain patents for "engines to drawe waters above their naturall Levill

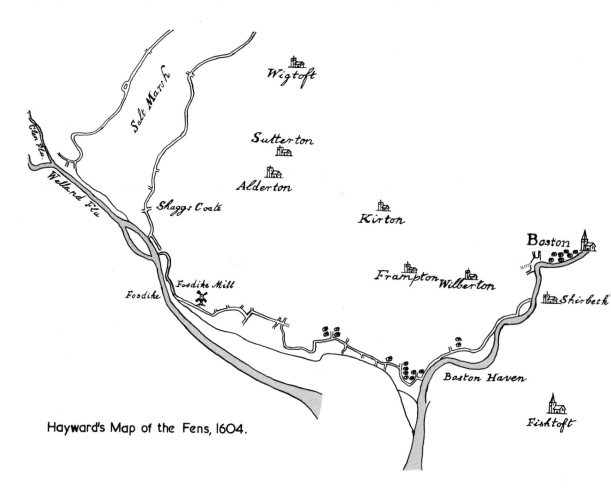

Hayward's Map of the Fens, 1604.

and to drayne waterishe and mooreishe grounds",[8] the most important and probably the earliest being Peter Morrice in 1575. His petition to "Mr. Fraunces Walshingham, principal Secretary to her excellent majesty", does not contain a description of the engine, and only states that

Peter Morrice yor poore orator hath to his extreme charge and with like payne travell and industrie endevored to make divers engins and instruments by motion whereof running streames and springes may be drawen farr higher than their naturall levills or course and also dead waters very likely to be drayned from the depths into other passages whereby the ground under them will prove firm and so moche the more fertill which thing if it comes to perfection will be a most high and great comoditie to the subjects of all partes of this realme . . . that it would please her M'gesty to grant unto him the seid patent to authorise him and his only to make and sel the same engines . . . forbiddinge all other . . . to make or use the same within thy realme unless it be by consent of the said Peter Morrice . . . for the term of 21 years.[9]

In 1578, Sir Thomas Goldinge asked for a patent for he claimed to be able by his engine "to drye all places drowned or under water"[10] and also "too convey water by great abundance into cities, townes, houses and all other places".[11] Daniel Houghesetter was more interested in draining mines, but his engine could be used for draining fens for it would raise "waters from anye place whatsoever from low to high".[12] There was William Mostart who applied in 1592 for the privilege alone "faire des engins pour secher les mares scayes et fennes basses".[13]

14

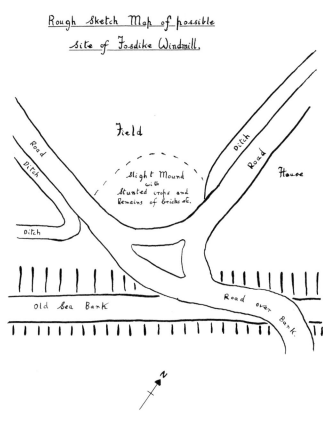

Rough Sketch Map of possible
Site of Fosdike Windmill.

Field

Slight Mound
with
Stunted crops and
Remains of bricks etc.

Ditch

Road

Ditch

Road

Ditch

House

Old Sea Bank

Road over Bank

N

Position, O.S. Map Sheet 123, Grid Reference 326332.

Far left: *Hayward's Map of the Fens (1604), Fosdike Mill*
Rough Sketch Map of Possible Site of Fosdike Mill

Peter Morrice failed to benefit from his patent and the rights were sold to George Carleton,[14] who proposed to set up his engines and drain grounds in the south of Ravens Dyke in the towns of Whaplode, Holbeach and Fleet.[15] It was felt that these "engines were dangerous to the countrie, of great charge and small performance, and experience hath well taught so",[16] and permission was not granted. He wanted to place one of the engines on the sea-bank between Gedney and Sutton Goates, an area now far inland. It would have been necessary to cut the bank to make the discharge sluice or goat for the engine, but it was claimed that this would seriously weaken the bank. Also it was feared that if he made his sluice 1 foot lower than the existing three sluices, the drainage through the others might be adversely affected.[17] It was felt that Carleton ought to be content with the existing drainage works and not try to improve his own lands at the expense of others. This was a view often repeated against windmills and even steam-engines so that the balance of the whole drainage system might not be upset by the individual. In Carleton's case it was felt that "the most part of all the other lowe grounds will be convenyently drayned by the old anncient and accustomed draynes, without any innovation, yf the same old draines were effectually repaired and amended".[18]

However, Carleton was able to erect some engines, for one came to an unfortunate end.

Holbech having an Ingen for them erected and sett upon the sea, to delyver their water had no greate dannger thereby. When the same standing but VIII tydes in chiefe of wynter took their ryver downe, and laid their goate drie. And as no danger; so no chardge, because the same was

15

geven by Mr. Carleton at his owne coste, as like now is offered for Sutton and, Gedney by such as shall draine that waie. Indeede that Ingyn had no contynuance because the fourth daie after the same was finished, and in her works, it was by the scheme of some wicked mynde overthrowen. . . . What Ingen soever that hath such handlinge cannot longe contynue but if such neighbourhood to the same had bene in Holland as Mr. Carleton fyndeth about Wisbech, Holland Ingyns might have prospered.[19]

The malefactor, William Stowe, was eventually apprehended and brought to trial. It appeared that

the said Stowe uppon Christes day last having no cause at all after prayer was ended in the church of Holbich called the dikereeves of that towne unto him, and ther in the Church said he marveyled yt they would suffer Toyes to be sett up uppon the sea banke to let the sea come in and not pull them downe? And therewithall with all seditious tearms departed the Church as greatlie grieved, saying to the people come and see and so drawinge therby manye about him he led them unto the Towne bridge there exclaiming in foule wourds and tearms against Mr. Carlton and the Ingens saying that he would spend all his land uppon Mr. Carlton and the dikereeves, because they suffered such Toyes to be set up, at which wourds when he saw none of the people take his parte, but were offended with him by soe saying, he went his way.

Item yt came to passe in the second night after, the Ingen yt stood uppon the sea having a beame in the water wourke, that bore the most part of the frame, standing upon yt conteininge about vij tunne of tymber was cut underneath in the myddle halfe asunder, saving one quarter of an ynch. And the next morning when the kepor thereof went to let her sayles goe, went up into her toppe to oyle her going geare for that end the north east wind blew from the sea and brake the said beame in the place so cutt and threwe downe bothe man and fframe.[20]

It is clear from this that the opposition to windmills was not general but confined to isolated people. In fact, the Privy Council seems to have looked favourably on them as a means of improving the Fens.[21] But Carleton soon found out the great drawback to windmills, that the wind to work them did not always blow at the right time.[22] Like many farmers after him, he waited in vain for a wind while his "groundes called Coldham, where he hath used all his pollicye and ingens, is at this Daie . . . drowned as ever it was".[23] While horses or men could be used to turn a small scoopwheel,[24] they did not have enough power to drain an extensive area, and so were not a practical substitute when the wind failed.

During the beginning of the seventeenth century, mills or engines were gradually introduced throughout the Fens. Richard Atkyns in a survey of the Fens in 1604 mentions certain grounds of Sir William Hindes at Over "where ther is an Ingin or Mill placed to raise water – and not farr fro there another mill for the town of Over, both serve to good purpose and empty the water into a dike which falleth into Willingham mere".[25] These mills are important because they show that some were already at work in the area which later came under the jurisdiction of the Bedford Level Corporation. Hayward's Map of the Fens shows a number of windmills scattered throughout the area, some being cornmills but a few may be for raising water. Casaubon saw one when he was travelling through the Fens with the Bishop of Ely in September 1611. They lost their way while returning from Wisbech and went to a windmill where they found a boy who showed them the right path to a ford. Here the Bishop's horse reared up and the Bishop fell off but came to no harm, although Casaubon took some hours to recover from the fright.[26] There was an engine or mill built at Leverington before 1617[27] and many more windmills, mostly on the silt lands, are shown on Sir William Dugdale's maps of the Fens published in 1662.

Up to this time, people had been mostly concerned with the silt lands, but the Bedford Level Corporation undertook to drain the peat lands. Under the first plan of 1630, the

16

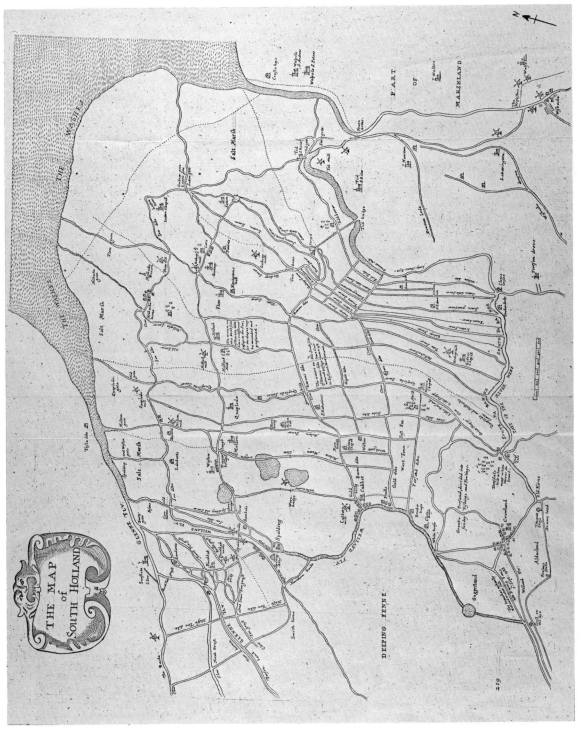

South Holland

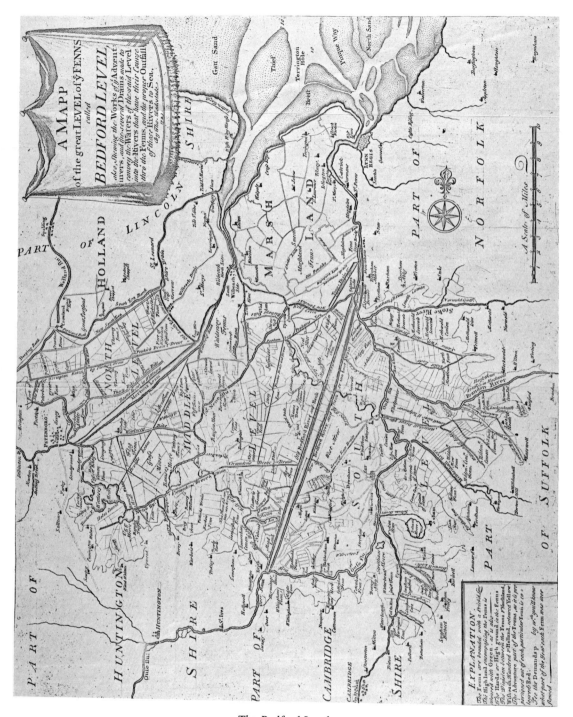

The Bedford Level

intention was to make "summer lands",[28] or lands which would be fit for grazing, but liable to be flooded in winter. The fourth Earl of Bedford and thirteen others agreed in the Indenture of Fourteen Parts to support the scheme financially. They were to divide 43,000 acres of fenland between themselves as a reward while 12,000 acres were to go to the King and a further 40,000 acres were to be set aside for income to maintain the works. Vermuyden contracted to drain, within six years, the peat lands and southern Fens which later became known as the Bedford Level. The chief works he undertook at this time were:

1. Bedford River (later called the Old Bedford River), extending from Earith to Salter's Lode Sluice, 70 feet wide and 21 miles in length.
2. Sam's Cut from Feltwell in Norfolk to the River Ouse.
3. A cut near Ely now called Sandy's Cut, 40 feet wide and 2 miles long.
4. Bevill's Leam from Whittlesey Mere to Guyhirne, 40 feet wide and 2 miles long.
5. Morton's Leam improved and remade.
6. Peakirk Drain from Peterborough Great Fen to Guyhirne, 17 feet wide, 10 miles long.
7. New South Eau, from Crowland to Clough's Cross.
8. Hill's Cut, near Peterborough, 50 feet wide and 2 miles long.
9. The Shire Drain from Clough's Cross to Tydd enlarged and improved.[29]

At a Session of Sewers held at St Ives, 12 October 1637, it was adjudged and declared "that the Earl of Bedford had at his own costs and charges, and with the expense of great sums of money, drained the said fenny and low grounds, according to the true intent of the Lynn Law".[30] Immediately after the passage of this St Ives Law, dissatisfaction appeared, and the decision was reversed in 1639 at Huntingdon by Royal Commission of Sewers. In 1649 a Pretended Act of Parliament[31] was passed authorizing William, fifth Earl and first Duke of Bedford, and his associates to drain the land so it would be fit for permanent agricultural use. Under this Act, the Bedford Level was divided into three parts, the North, Middle and South Levels, each with its own Board of Commissioners to supervise their area. Vermuyden was again placed in charge of the works, but he did not carry out his plan for the South Level. This was to dig a channel round the eastern edge of the Fens to intercept the water in the rivers and take it to the sea so it never came into the lowland at all. This idea has been frequently revived and is being carried out at the present time. However, Vermuyden was able to cut another drain parallel to the Bedford River called the New Bedford River or the Hundred Foot River. This was tidal, while the Old Bedford River had a sluice at the end. Denver Sluice was built in 1651 to keep the tides out of the old course of the Ouse and thereby lessen the danger to the banks of the South Level. Other works undertaken at this time were Downham Eau from Denver Sluice to Stowbridge, Popham's Eau cleaned and revived, Vermuyden's or the Forty Foot Drain that ran from Ramsey to the Old Bedford River at Welches Dam. Some other drains were also made near March and Whittlesey, Moore's Drain and Stonea Drain, Hammond's Eau near Somersham and Conquest Lode leading to Whittlesey Mere.[32] Most of these drains were in the Middle Level and some improvements were made in the Duke of Bedford's own lands in the North Level, but the South Level was not really tackled. Vermuyden left the Fens in 1655, to try his skill elsewhere, perhaps because he saw that his full plans would not be carried out, but he has left behind him a permanent mark on the drainage of this area.

The Pretended Act was confirmed by a fresh Act which received the Royal Assent on 13 September 1660[33] on the restoration of Charles II. But after the initial improvement in drainage throughout the Great Level that followed the completion of these works, there followed the inevitable slow decline as the peat gradually wasted away. It became more

Acre Fen Mill, 20-foot Drain, Chatteris (Reid Collection)

difficult to find people willing to invest their money in an undertaking that was proving so risky. The Corporation found that it could barely maintain the existing works, let alone initiate new ones. The banks, which had been made mostly of peat, were inadequate, and the rivers steadily deteriorated. Everywhere there was more work to be done than there was money available. For example, in 1701 Mr John Reynolds, Steward to the Duke of Bedford, informed the Corporation "that the money allotted this yeare for the Workes of the North Levell is not sufficient to putt the Workes of the said Levell in a defencible condicion against any ordinary flood that may happen".[34] Sometimes the Corporation was forced to employ the doubtful expedient of using funds that had been allocated for somewhere else, or completing the work on the credit of the following year's taxes.[35]

More and more, farmers found that they had to resort to artificial means of drainage. At a meeting of the Bedford Level Corporation in London in May 1663, there was an application from John Trafford to drain 500 acres of fen at Tydd St Maries by an engine into the Clough's Cross Drain. Permission was granted "so long as the same be not prejudiciall to the venting of the waters of the Great Levell of the ffens called Bedford Levell".[36] In later Minutes there are other references to engines or mills. Sometimes permission was being sought to erect an engine,[37] but more usually there was a complaint against a particular mill. Often there was a certain amount of self-interest in the action taken when the mill

20

concerned threatened the Corporation's lands. An interesting case in 1680 was over some mills in Coldham and Waldersea, "whereby the Adventurers grounds there abouts were much dampnified".[38] The offending mills were not ordered to be pulled down, but a bank was made to prevent the water thrown out by the mills running into the Adventurers grounds of Lades and Crooks.[39] The result was that "by reason of the said bank, the said inhabitants were in a very badd condition having noo other ways at present to vent their mill waters whereby theyr grounds would become useless and the present crops thereon bee utterly spoiled".[40] They therefore asked that they might be able to cut a watercourse through the bank as a temporary expedient until they could find some other way of draining before the following spring.

Mills continued to be set up without any supervision and the nuisance they caused greatly increased. Lord Torrington proposed setting up two mills in the Whittlesey area that threatened the Adventurers lands,[41] and there were a great many other mills in that district. One of the Corporation's officers, Mr Bourne, was ordered to find out how many mills there were on Moore's Drain and Bevill's River, what size they were and to whom they belonged.[42] In 1698 great harm and destruction was "committed by divers desparate and malicious persons, that have destroyed in a great measure the works of draining in Deeping Level . . . under cover and pretence of football playing".[43] Houses, buildings, mills, banks and other works of draining were destroyed, and the Bedford Level Corporation was warned that the rioters intended to meet at Coates Green near Whittlesey to pull down the mills and cut the banks, again under cover of "Football Play and other sports".[44]

Perhaps as a result of these riots, the Bedford Level Corporation took active measures against horse-mills and windmills. In its capacity as a Court of Sewers, the Corporation in three recorded sessions in 1700, 1701 and 1708[45] fined, or ordered to be stopped up, forty-four windmills and thirty-seven horse-mills. The indictment varied little at each of these sessions, a typical one being that against John Walsham in 1700.

Wherefore it was the same day presented by the same jury that John Walsham, gent, for working his engine or mill which through mudd and stuffe into the 20ty. ffoote Draine called Mooree Drayne so Mudd and stuffe choaked and stopped the currant of the water of the said drayne in its passage to the River Neane and therefore prayed that the said John Walsham may be enjoyned by the authority of this Court not to worke the said engine or mill on this side and before the — day of — next and in default thereof to forfeite to the King's Majesty's use the sum of 10/– if he shall doe the same, ordered the same to be stopped accordingly.[46]

John Walsham was brought before the Court on all three occasions, and half a dozen others appear twice, although the fine was increased to £100 in 1701.[47] None of these mills was ordered to be removed, for this was beyond the powers of the Bedford Level Corporation. All were charged with causing an obstruction in the rivers or drains, and therefore had to pay a fine or cease from working. The number of windmills continued to increase for they had become a necessity by this time.

Windmills could be used by anyone provided there were no complaints, and this is made perfectly clear in two court cases about this time. The case of Sylas Titus was not to try whether the owners of mills had a right to work and use them,[48] for it was acknowledged that they were free to build and erect mills, but the point at dispute was whether mill-owners could use their own machines if they damaged or drowned their neighbours' lands while they drained their own.[49] The point was that nobody should "erect or make any works for draining, at their own wills and pleasures, their own lands to the damage of public draining, and the prejudice of other lands adjacent upon any pretence whatsoever".[50] It was felt that people should be content with the usual way of draining, provided by the Conservators of the Bedford Level, and so the owners had to pay the fines imposed upon them because they had blocked up the drains.[51]

Where there was no nuisance, the Bedford Level Corporation could do nothing, and this principle is borne out in the case against Mr Hyde. In 1699 he applied for permission to build a mill to throw the water from Sutton St Edmund into the Shire Drain. Although this area is not in the Bedford Level, the Corporation were responsible for the drain, for it carried away the waters of the North Level. A committee was appointed to view the place and permission was to be given if its report decided that the mill would not obstruct the water flowing from the North Level.[52] But there must have been some other opposition, for the Bedford Level Corporation started to prepare a case for Counsel.[53] After alternately being granted permission to build a mill in various places and then having it withdrawn,[54] Mr Hyde decided to go ahead and start building. Officers of the North Level ordered the workmen to stop erecting the mill but they continued to work.[55] The Corporation was resolved to obstruct this mill throwing its water into the Shire Drain, so advice was sought from Counsel.[56] The Corporation was probably advised to see if this mill did in fact block up the Shire Drain, so orders were given for the water-level to be carefully observed. One of the Corporation's officers, Mr Le Pla, claimed that the mill did raise the water,[57] but he could not have had time to take accurate measurements. After this the whole affair died down. At London it was decided to consider it another time,[58] while the Ely Proceedings show that Mr Hyde wanted witnesses appointed from both sides to view the Shire Drain when his mill was working to report whether it affected the water-level.[59] Since there were no further proceedings, it is clear that the Shire Drain was well able to "bear the Waters of St. Edmund"[60] as had been earlier suggested and the windmill remained for it did not cause a nuisance.

There were further riots and disturbances against windmills,[61] but the riots died down and the number of windmills increased. Mr Richard Saffery received permission direct from the Corporation to erect a mill on the north bank of the New Bedford River between the Wash and the Old Bedford River so he could drain his lands better.[62] The inhabitants of Cottenham were allowed to build a mill or engine on Chear Fen bank between Sir Roger Jenyns's mill and Twenty Pence Ferry to drain their water into the River Ouse provided they made good any damage they should do to the Corporation's works.[63] Sir Roger Jenyns was a Conservator who had defended the Bedford Level Corporation against Sylas Titus, but he himself possessed a mill at that time or soon afterwards. It was not much use to him, for when Badeslade went to look at those parts, he took a boat at Stretham Ferry and "went to Sir *Roger Jennyn's* Engine Mile, which is placed upon a great drain belonging to *Cottenham*; those very lands which this Engine is intended to drain, (and which was heretofore rich Meadow) we found drowned".[64]

The Bedford Level found itself facing increasing indebtedness as it struggled to keep the waterways and banks in repair especially around 1725 when there was a series of very wet years.[65] In the South Level, the situation was probably made worse when Denver Sluice was undermined and blown up by the tides in 1713. There was no money to repair it (it was not rebuilt till 1746) and the extra expenses entailed by many great floods in the two years before March 1726 ran the Corporation into heavy debt. The country under its care suffered calamitously, for the whole area was under water most of that time as the outfalls to the sea were obstructed.[66] Badeslade states quite clearly that were it "not for a great number of Landholders throwing the Fen Waters over Banks into the River and Drains, by Engines made at their own Expense, they say, the whole Body of the Fens would become unprofitable; and Taxes enough could not be raised to maintain the Works, and to pay Salaries".[67]

Since the windmill had become essential if large parts of the Fens were to be preserved from inundation, and since it was possible to obtain permission to erect them from the Bedford Level Corporation, the question must be asked why was it necessary for the Haddenham Level to go to the trouble and expense of obtaining an Act of Parliament for draining that particular part of the Fens? The evidence given before Parliament by John Clark, James Fortry, Mr Walker and John Kent stressed that the Level had long been drowned and that the only remedy was drainage by mills or engines.[68] But in the correspondence with the Bedford Level Corporation, mills or engines were never mentioned. In April 1726 the inhabitants of Haddenham sent a petition to the Ely Conservators complaining that the bank of the Hundred Foot River was too low, for the floods had come over it twice during the last winter and greatly damaged their land. They asked that the banks should be raised and some way found to improve the outfalls to the sea.[69] In the following April a similar petition was presented complaining this time about the north bank of the Ouse between the Hermitage and Stretham Ferry, and also about the state of some of the ditches.[70] From this time to 1731, the Bedford Level Corporation spent over £400 on the banks of the Haddenham area, but, in the meantime, permission had been given by the London Committee of the Bedford Level Corporation for the inhabitants of Haddenham to drain their lands "at their own expense".[71] No objection was raised so an Act was promoted and passed.[72]

Immediately afterwards, this example was followed by the areas of Whittlesey and Waterbeach. Before a Committee of the House of Commons in February 1728, Mr George Claxon said that,

the low Lands, and Fen Grounds, in the Township of *Whittlesey*, containing Seven thousand Acres, or there abouts, have until of late, been very good, and yielded great Profit; but the same, for the Space of Seven Years last past, and upwards, have been so often drowned: and surrounded with Waters, that the same have yielded little or no Profit to the Owners: That he has Fifteen Acres in the said low Lands, but has made nothing thereof for these Three Years; but had formerly Six Pounds a Year: That he believes, that the cause of the said low Lands being drowned is the Want of proper inland Drains, and embanking the old Drains, and raising proper Engines, for throwing the Waters into the common Rivers.[73]

The Waterbeach Level also sent a petition to Parliament[74] but their Bill was never read when the Whittlesey Bill failed to pass beyond the Committee stage.[75] It is not known whether this was the result of opposition or whether the initiators had gained what they wanted, for about £600 was spent by the Bedford Level Corporation on the banks of the Waterbeach Level before 1732.[76] Another reason may have been the promise of a general scheme for the Fens as various ones were suggested during the next few years (e.g. Armstrong, Labelye).[77] The years 1729 to 1731 did see an improvement in conditions,[78] but it is suspected that there must have been some opposition or legal hitch because the next successful drainage Bill was not passed until 1738, for the very small area of Redmore, Waterden and Cawdle Fens near Ely.[79] This Act was followed soon after by a second application from the Waterbeach Level in 1741[80] which was this time successful. From then on, many other areas procured their own individual drainage Acts from Parliament.

These Acts authorized the establishment of Boards of Commissioners who would be responsible for the internal drainage of their districts. They were empowered "to make such Cuts, Drains, Damms and Outlets, through the said Fens and Low Grounds . . . and to make and erect such Works and Engines thereupon, for draining and conveying the Waters from the same".[81] In order to maintain all these works, they could levy an annual tax, usually about a shilling per acre. This was made a statutory demand, based on ownership of the land, with powers of seizure for non-payment. There were other sections concerning the cleansing of drains, and penalties laid down against anyone who should destroy any of the mills or engines or obstruct any of the drains or other works.[82] With such an Act, an area could obtain legal protection for any work carried out, and compel the occupiers of the land to subscribe towards such work, so it was at last possible to have as competent a drainage system as the limits of windmills allowed.

NOTES

1. R. J. Forbes, *Studies in Ancient Technology* (1955), vol. II, p. 60.
2. B.L.C., Records of Earlier Courts of Sewers, 19 Rich. II, see also 21 Hen. VIII.
3. Harleian MS., 701, p. 30.
4. ibid., pp. 25 and 30.
5. See Acts of Parliament, e.g. Haddenham Level, 13 Geo. I, c. 18 (1727), and Waterbeach Level, 14 Geo. II, c. 24 (1741).
6. Harleian MS., 5011/41 and B.L.C., Records of Earlier Courts of Sewers, 15 Jam. I.
7. M. Kirkus, *The Records of the Commissioners of Sewers . . .* (1959), p. 29. Records for 26 January 1555.
8. S.P., Dom. Eliz., 106/62.
9. ibid.
10. ibid.
11. ibid.
12. Lansdowne MS., 110/3.
13. S.P., Dom. Eliz., 241/114.
14. Acts of the Privy Council, 26 June 1580, pp. 68–9.
   That whereas her Majestie had by her Letters Patentes licenced one Peter Morris to draine certaine fennes and lowe groundes surrounded with waters by certaine engines and devicses never knowen or used before, which beinge putt in practise by George Carlton and Humfrey Michell, esquiors, unto [whom] the said Morris for want of habilitie had conveyed over his said Letters Patentes, were like to prove verie commodious and beneficiall unto the countreye and Realme, in case the same workes begun might be finished, which are said to be now greatlie hindered for want of workmen and labourers to be had in season convenient.
15. Lansdowne MS., 41/46, p. 181.
16. ibid., 41/49, p. 195.
17. ibid., 41/46, p. 181.
18. ibid., 41/49, p. 199.
19. ibid., 41/49, p. 203.
20. S.P., Dom. Eliz., 219/73.
21. Lansdowne MS., 41/49, p. 203.
22. R. D'Acres, *The Art of Water Drawing* (1659), p. 8.
23. Lansdowne MS., 46/56, p. 113.
24. W. Blith, *The English Improver Improved* (2nd ed. 1652), p. 56.
25. Harleian MS., 5011/41, also Ely Diocesan Records, Fen Drainage Bundle, p. 282.
26. I. Casaubon, *Ephemerides* (1611), vol. II, p. 866.
27. B.L.C., Records of Earlier Courts of Sewers, 15 Jam. I.
28. S. Wells, *The History of the Drainage of . . . Bedford Level* (1830), vol. I, p. 118.
29. H. C. Darby, *The Draining of the Fens* (1940), p. 40.
30. S. Wells, op. cit., p. 118.
31. ibid. for the Pretended Act passed on 29 May 1649.
32. H. C. Darby, op. cit., p. 74. L. E. Harris, *Vermuyden and the Fens* (1953), pp. 114–17.
33. 15 Char. II, c. 17.
34. B.L.C., London, 3 July 1701.
35. B.L.C., Ely, 23 July 1725.
   Ordered that the forty pounds allotted in the said Estimate for the Scouring out Haddenham Drain be employed in the repairing of the said Banks of Burnt Fen Level in case the said Haddenham Drain cannot be scoured out this year. But if the said drain can be scoured out this year then the officer for that Division is hereby Impowered to lay out the sum of fforty pounds in repairing the said Banks and to bring the same into his next years Estimate by way of Debt.
36. B.L.C., London, 8 May 1663.
37. ibid., 18 August 1664.
38. ibid., 8 December 1680.

39. ibid., 1 December 1681.
40. ibid.
41. ibid., 19 and 31 August 1693, see also 28 May 1696 for an attempt to set up a mill near Whittlesey.
42. ibid., 31 August 1693.
43. ibid., 7 March 1698.
44. ibid.
45. B.L.C. as Commissioners of Sewers, 1700, 1701, 1708.
46. ibid., 5 March 1700.
47. ibid., 28 March 1701.
48. S. Wells, op. cit., p. 435.
49. ibid., p. 429.
50. ibid., p. 431.
51. B.L.C., London, 6 February 1706.
52. ibid., 11 July 1699.
53. ibid., 30 November 1699.
54. ibid., 11 July, 30 November, 7, 14, 26 December 1669 and 27 February 1700.
55. ibid., 5 December 1701.
56. ibid.
57. ibid., 25 March 1703.
58. ibid.
59. B.L.C., Ely, 9 April 1703.
60. B.L.C., London, 26 December 1699.
61. ibid., 18 February 1702/3.
    Whereas wee are now credibly informed by the said John Wakelin and others that there has lately been a Rising of Severall disorderly persons who have lately pulled downe and distroyed a Windmill or Water Engine belonging to one Mrs. Keat within the said Levell, We doe order the said John Wakelin that he doth from time to time use his utmost endeavours as much as possibly he can to Suppress and hinder all such Mobbs and Riotous meetings.
62. ibid., 14 December 1721.
63. B.L.C., Ely, 8 April 1727.
64. T. Badeslade, *The History . . . of the Navigation of . . . King's-Lyn* (1725), p. 93, 26 January 1723.
65. See Chap. I, note 1.
66. B.L.C., London, 16 March 1726.
67. T. Badeslade, op. cit., p. 94.
68. *Journal of the House of Commons*, 2 March 1726/7, quoted in full in H. C. Darby, op. cit.
69. B.L.C., Ely, 9 April 1726.
70. ibid., 7 April 1727.
71. B.L.C., London, 2 March 1726/7.
72. 13 Geo. I, c. 18.
73. *Journal of the House of Commons*, 20 February 1728, see also 7 February 1728.
74. ibid., 19 and 28 February 1728.
75. ibid., 20 February 1728.
76. B.L.C., Ely, April 1726, 1729 and 1731.
77. Colonel J. Armstrong, *History of the Navigation of King's Lynn* (1725), and C. Labelye, *Result of a View of the Great Level of the Fens . . .* (1745) which includes T. Badeslade, *A Scheme for draining the Great Level of the Fens . . .* (1729).
78. *Journal of the House of Commons*, 6 March 1737.
79. 11 Geo. II, c. 34.
80. 14 Geo. II, c. 24.
81. Act for Haddenham Level, 13 Geo. I, c. 18.
82. ibid.

CHAPTER III

Gentle Spectators

In the days before the coming of the railway, the Fens had a system of internal communications unequalled in Britain, yet the full potential of river transport, and indeed of every aspect of fenland economy, had still to be realized. Even by the end of the eighteenth century large parts of the country had scarcely progressed from producing only reeds and swamps, and were liable to revert at any moment to their former primitive state. It is true that there were a few signs of the revolution that was to take place in the first half of the nineteenth century, but a brief glance at the state of the rivers at the turn of the century will show how much had to be done.

The rivers did of course carry a great volume of trade and traffic. The extent of this, both in variety and destination, is shown by Kinderley.

This River [Ouse], by its Situation, and having so many navigable Rivers falling into it from eight several Counties, does therefore afford a great Advantage to Trade and Commerce, since hereby two Cities and several great Towns are therein served; as *Peterborough, Ely, Stamford, Bedford, St. Ives, Huntingdon, St. Neots, Northampton, Cambridge, Bury St. Edmunds, Thetford*, etc. with all sorts of heavy commodities from *Lyn*; as Coals and Salt (from *Newcastle*) Deals, Fir-Timber, Iron, Pitch, and Tar (from *Sweden* and *Norway*) and Wine (from *Lisbon* and *Oporto*) thither imported; and from these Parts great Quantities of Wheat, Rye, Cole-seed, Oats, Barley are brought down these Rivers, whereby a great foreign and inland Trade is carried on, and the Breed of Seamen is increased.[1]

Export of agricultural produce and import of coal and timber remained the basic pattern of fenland trade, but it was conducted through rivers that were barely navigable. Although Robert Mylne thought the navigation of the Cam between Clayhithe and Jesus Green "to be the most defective in the kingdom",[2] conditions in most of the other fen rivers were similar.[3] His report on the lower part below Clayhithe shows that it was barely possible to navigate, and he only just succeeded in getting his own boat through. Rivers that were too shallow for boats could not carry the volume of water that came down from the highlands in times of flood, so it was in the interests of both drainage and navigation that Mylne made his report.

I found only eleven inches of water, on the tail of Clayhithe Sluice, although there had been but some hours before all the waters in the three reaches between the locks [above Clayhithe] let off in a spendthrift manner, to form thereby a *flash*, to enable some gangs of boats to pass out of *Clayhithe* Sluice, and downwards over and through the shoals, as far as the junction of the *Grant* and *Old Ouze*. This opportunity was taken by some going up, but they were caught aground at the ford above mentioned; and even if they had got to the hole at the tail of *Clayhithe*, they could not possibly get *into* the sluice without another such flash or flood in the river.

The outfalls of the rivers to the sea were in an equally deplorable condition. A fuller account of their state and how this was remedied will be given later, but a quick glance will suffice to show what they were like at the beginning of the nineteenth century. Much of our information comes from John Rennie who played an important role in the develop-

SOUNDING OF DEPTH OF WATER IN RIVERS OUZE AND GRANTA, OCT. 1791, by R. Mylne

ft.	ins.	
5.	0.	at Ely Bridge.
3.	6.	at mouth of Grant.
2.	6.	Dimocks Coates houses.
2.	4.	at the staunch tried three years ago at Reach Lode.
2.	0.	hard bottom, gentle stream opposite Swaffham Lode.
2.	0.	hard sandy bottom at Botsham Lode.
1.	4.	a gang of 9 boats stopped aground.
0.	8.	My boat stopped, lightened her at a ford half a mile below Clayhithe. 10 boats stopped aground drawing 2 feet water at Toll House.
2.	0.	above Toll House.
0.	8.	At cill of gates, Clayhithe Sluice.[4]

ment of the Fens. He was well suited for this, not only by his early mechanical training in windmills and steam-engines, but his work on canals gave him useful experience in dealing with hydraulic problems. He thus possessed unique qualifications of which the fenmen were quick to take advantage, and in 1802 he was asked to survey the River Witham. He found that the gates of the Grand Sluice at Boston were completely silted up and no water was passing down the river. Half the water was drawn off the river above Lincoln to supply lockage for boats going along the Fossdike Canal to the Trent, while the water that flowed below Lincoln was used to supply the cattle in the Fens. There was not enough water left to keep the river scoured.[5] Although parts of the river were over 2½ feet deep, Rennie found that above Kirkstead Lock some places were only 1 foot 5 inches deep.[6] The Welland was equally bad so "no vessels except barges could reach Spalding at all".[7] Both the Witham and the Welland wandered across shifting sands in numerous small streams for many miles and had no proper deep channel to the sea.[8]

The mouth of the Nene was also shallow so that the Wisbech navigation and trade could be continued only under great difficulties and risks. "Ships of large burden could no longer reach the town, and had been exchanged for a humbler class of vessels, from 40 to 60 tons burden, and even these were frequently neaped within a few miles of the town for two or three weeks, and sometimes for a longer period."[9] The trouble here was the mass of shifting sands which lay between Wisbech and the sea, and the narrow and confined channel through the town of Wisbech itself so that the floods could not pass off properly.[10] The Ouse presented an equally pitiable picture. Although trade was adversely affected by the Napoleonic Wars, everyone agreed that Lynn Harbour had grown much worse within living memory, and ships were finding it more difficult to reach the harbour from the sea.[11] For about four miles above the harbour, the channel was very wide and bent round in a complete semicircle.[12] Here the force of the current was lost as the water wandered across sand- and mud-banks which frequently moved their positions. Barges and lighters were often held up for as long as two weeks[13] and many were sunk. But more important was the effect on the drainage, for the sand-banks held up the flood water and prevented it reaching the sea.[14]

While on one side the water could not escape from the Fens through the outfalls, on the other, agricultural improvements in the highlands sent the flood waters down to the Fens more quickly and violently than before.[15] Instead of the water lying on the open fields until it had evaporated, the great number of new enclosures in the upland counties brought

27

Isleham Mill
(*Reid Collection*)

improved drainage to the land so that much of the rain passed straight into the rivers without any hindrance. Therefore water ran down to the Fens more quickly and fenmen complained of the suddenness of the floods as compared with former periods, "insomuch that eight hours of heavy rain will bring a flood".[16] This evil was increasing as the numbers of enclosures in the highlands advanced, while the land-level in the Fens fell through the efforts made to drain it. The fenmen found themselves in a rapidly deteriorating situation, and even while they argued among themselves about what they should do, the outfalls became more and more choked.[17] These external factors, coupled with the gradual sinking of the land, were rapidly making the windmill a completely inadequate machine for drainage.

The windmills used in the Fens were nearly always built of wood. Usually they had four sails, although there was one with six at Daintree and Daniel Defoe describes a model of one with twelve, but he did not see this working.[18] The sails of the largest mills were 96 feet from tip to tip and were covered with canvas, but there was no method of furling the cloth without stopping the mill. In order to compensate for the constantly changing wind pressure, in 1772 Meikle invented and patented the spring sail with shutters. Each sail still had to be adjusted individually which meant stopping the mill, but in 1807 Sir William Cubitt improved the apparatus and arranged for the shutters to be adjusted at one operation without stopping the mill.[19] In spite of its apparent advantages, this device does not appear to have been used on the drainage mills in the Fens. This may have been due to expense or perhaps the men who operated the mills had more time to adjust the set of the sails because

28

they had no other duties such as grinding corn. Likewise the fantail, or the small sail at the back of the mill for keeping the head turned automatically into the wind, does not seem to have been used. Instead three lever beams from the head of the mill, reaching almost to the ground, joined together at the bottom where there was a winch. A chain attached to the winch could be fixed to the heads of piles of which there were ten or twelve round the base of the mill, so the mill could be turned to face the wind as occasion demanded.

The mill was built on piles driven through the peat into the clay, and English mills were usually boarded on the outside, not thatched like many Dutch ones. The space inside was severely restricted by the gear-wheels that drove the pumping machinery. In England this was almost invariably a scoopwheel which worked in a brick trough outside the body of the mill and might have a wooden cover over it.[20] Some of the Dutch wheels and some of the smaller English ones were set inside the mills. Figures given by Mr Wailes show that the diameter of a scoopwheel could be as great as 25 feet, as at Soham Mere, and photographs and drawings of other mills show wheels of nearly this diameter. The lift of a scoopwheel was effective to about one-fifth of its diameter, and therefore limited to 4 or at the most 5 feet.[21] The mills could only pump out about 3 foot of water from the land, for when the ladles had a dip of about 1 foot they could not throw out much water.[22]

Two men would usually work one of these mills, or perhaps one man with the assistance of his family. They would be allowed to live rent-free in the mill, even during the summer when the mills were "set down" and not used. There might be various repairs which had to be carried out during this period for which the millers received pay, or sometimes the mills would have to be worked in an emergency. Otherwise the millers only received a wage during the winter when the mills were actually working. The variableness of their earnings is shown by the figures given below, which are the totals of the sums paid as wages at each of the windmills in the Haddenham Level. Usually there were two men, but the Sutton mill may have been attended by a family.

Year.	Highbridge.	Horseshoe.	Ferry.	Lazier.	Sutton.
1739–40	7. 18. 0	7. 19. 0	7. 17. 0	5. 19. 0	7. 13. 5
40/41	7. 0. 0	6. 18. 0	6. 10. 0	8. 1. 0	4. 9. 11
43/44	4. 13. 0	5. 9. 6	4. 0. 6	4. 12. 0	2. 10. 6
44/45	14. 8. 0	16. 16. 0	14. 8. 0	14. 8. 0	8. 6. 0[23]

Besides living free in the mills, there was a further bounty of free fuel. The Haddenham Level Account Books show that turf or peat was sent to the mills, and later coals were given instead. This tradition survived until well into the present century, for the stokers and superintendents of the steam-engines also received free coal. At the end of the eighteenth century, the millers received 10s. 6d. a week with coals,[24] and they were ordered to work whenever there was a strong enough wind, even during the night. Normally they would be responsible only for working the mill, although they might be employed casually on other odd jobs when the mills were set down. George Carleton expected his miller to do considerably more and was going to give him a separate house to be

builded under Sutton Sea banke upon some convenyent place for a man to dwell in, to keepe the Engen going in wynter, to looke to the Doares of all the Sleuces and goates as well Gedney Sutton as the new workes, and to spend his whole yere else in scouringe the channell; clensing the ffynnes and creeks, repayringe the two creestees upon the marshes, and taking the charges of coale, tymber or whatsoever else shall be upon that wharfe unladen by shippe or carte.[25]

Later it was laid down for some areas by Act of Parliament that "no trees, stacks of hay fodder turf etc. or buildings shall be erected or built nearer to any Mill or Engine than

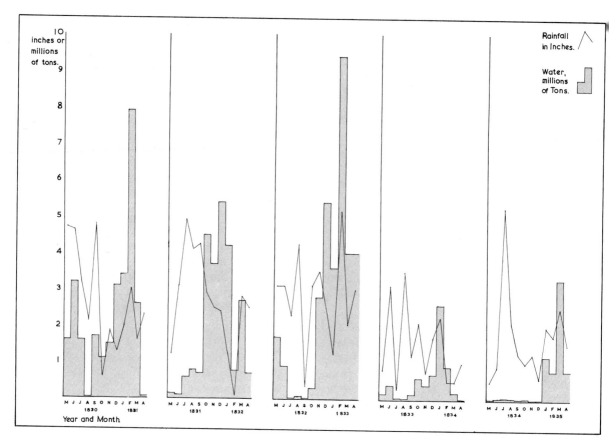

Rainfall
in Inches.

Water,
millions
of Tons.

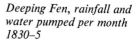

Year and Month.

Deeping Fen, rainfall and
water pumped per month
1830–5

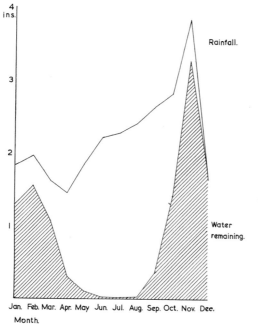

Rainfall.

Water
remaining.

Rainfall and evaporation rates
from Dempsey's figures

Jan. Feb. Mar. Apr. May Jun. Jul. Aug. Sep. Oct. Nov. Dec.
Month.

fifty yards".[26] This meant the men had to live inside their mills, and although to our minds these dwellings would have seemed dark and cramped, they were probably as good as the house of an agricultural labourer at that period. Usually there were no windows, and the smoke from the fire had to make its way out through cracks in the top of the mill, but this served a good purpose for the smoke helped to preserve the wood. At the end of the eighteenth century, one of the larger windmills would cost more than £1,000 to erect. The Waterbeach Level paid £1,300 in 1814, and Arthur Young mentions one at Wilmington for £1,400 and two at Wisbech, which were rated at 9 h.p., for £1,200 each.[27]

It is very difficult to assess the amount of water that had to be pumped out by the windmills. There was rain or snow that fell on the fenland itself, there was water that ran from the uplands into the low-lying parts, and there was water that soaked through the banks. Some fen areas were completely isolated from higher land so had only rain or soakage to consider, and in other places catchwater drains were dug to cut off the water coming from the highland before it reached the fen. The river-banks were all too often made of peat or other light soil so that they were porous and let water into the fen. This was especially so in a high flood when "the banks in a night let as much water soak back through the banks as all the mills can throw into the river even when the winds blow".[28] The volume of water from this source cannot be estimated for it depended upon the condition of the banks, but it must have been quite considerable.

The amount that fell as rain can be estimated from later records, but few figures were kept before the year 1800. The total in any individual year might vary between 12 and 30 inches, but an average of the years 1840 to 1925 at the Stretham engine in the Waterbeach Level works out at 21·21 inches per annum. Even John Rennie had "no correct account of the Total quantity of rain that falls on the surface averagely in the year, on Deeping Fen, but from experiments made in other places similarly situated, it cannot be reckoned at less than twenty Inches, and of this quantity, instances can be produced of two inches falling in the course of one day".[29] The amount of water to be pumped out depended upon the rate of evaporation, and this depended upon the state of the soil and the type of vegetation. The following figures worked out around 1850[30] show considerable agreement with a table supplied recently by the Rijnland Drainage Board from Holland (see Appendix IX).

Month	Total falling	Evaporated	Remaining	Waterbeach Records, averages of rainfall 1840 to 1925
January	1·847	·540	1·307	1·38
February	1·971	·424	1·547	1·07
March	1·617	·540	1·077	1·26
April	1·456	1·150	·306	1·36
May	1·856	1·748	·108	1·56
June	2·213	2·174	·039	1·90
July	2·287	2·245	·024	2·46
August	2·427	2·391	·036	2·37
September	2·639	2·270	·369	1·96
October	2·823	1·423	1·400	2·22
November	3·837	·579	3·258	1·72
December	1·641	·164	1·805	1·62
	26·614	15·320	11·294	20·88

It will·be noticed, especially from the Waterbeach Level Records, how the greater part of the rain fell in the summer months when most of it would be evaporated. Therefore the amount of rain to be pumped out is not so great as at first appears, although the other sources of incoming water must not be forgotten.

As the amount of water that needed to be pumped out varied considerably from year to year, so did the time that the windmills were used. They were seldom worked for less than six months and often for eight or nine,[31] and they were normally set down and not worked during the summer when most of the rain was evaporated. Usually in summer-time there was not enough wind to drive the mills, although in 1789 there was enough wind to keep the two windmills of Middle Fen near Ely at work all the season for the summer was very wet. It will be remembered how George Carleton had found that his lands were drowned and his engines useless, presumably because there was no wind,[32] and many other writers comment that "we have but too much reason to fear the winds will not be commanded when we stand in need of them".[33] William Swansborough, an experienced fen engineer of the early nineteenth century reckoned that the windmills worked upon an average one day in five,[34] for a considerable wind velocity was necessary before the mills could work effectively. Joseph Nickalls states that "the force of wind, acting equal to the strength of four horses was unable to open the water-gate or door".[35] The size of windmills varied enormously so that very few figures are given of their performance. The best windmills in 1814 would raise 2,000 cubic feet of water per minute when the difference in levels did not exceed 5 feet 6 inches,[36] and a large windmill was expected to drain about 1,000 acres of land. James Watt reckoned that a 10 h.p. steam-engine would be needed to raise 500 cubic feet of water 5 feet per minute and it could work continuously.[37] From this it would seem that the best fen windmills were producing about 40 h.p. when there was sufficient wind.

Tests have been carried out in Holland on some windmills before any attempt was made to modernize them with streamlined sails or other improvements, so the following figures would probably be characteristic of other old mills including those in the Fens. With a wind speed of 5 to 6 metres per second (about 12 m.p.h.), a windmill started to turn, but only very slowly, the scoopwheel displacing hardly any water, just enough to open the sluice door in front. As the wind increased to over 8 metres (18 m.p.h.) the mill in full sail would begin to work well and soon reach its maximum safe revolutions of 75 to 80 "ends" (the number of tips of sails passing each minute). The mill would be producing somewhere around 50 h.p., but only about half of this was given off by the scoopwheel even if all the components were in good condition. As the wind gathered strength, from about 10 metres per second onwards (23 m.p.h.), the miller would have to reef the sails, and at 12 metres per second (27 m.p.h.) he would work with the sail cloths furled. With any stronger wind, the mill would have to be stopped, for it would be doing about 90 "ends" and there was a danger of it running away. The scoopwheel would then rotate at too high a speed and the water would splash to the sides or whirl round so that the scoops did not fill properly. This would not give sufficient load to the mill, and there was a risk that everything would go to pieces.[38]

A windmill will work with wind speeds varying from 6 to 12 metres per second, but the ideal is from 8 to 10 metres per second. In Holland the wind may be expected to have a speed of between 6 and 8 metres for 1,332 hours on an average each year, and during 1,339 hours there will be wind between 8 and 12 metres.[39] In England, using recent figures taken by the Meteorological Station at Mildenhall, the respective hours are approximately 1,778 and 450. The total 2,671 hours for Holland and 2,238 for England when the windmills might be able to do some work. However, in England there is very much less wind over 8 metres per second, only 450 hours as compared with 1,339 in Holland, so that the time

ANALYSIS OF WIND VELOCITY COMPILED FROM HOURLY TABULATIONS, METEOROLOGICAL STATION, MILDENHALL, 1950 to 1959.

Mean Wind Speed, m/sec	Beaufort Scale Equivalent	Total hours in percentages	
0·3		2·7	
0·3– 1·5	1	19·2	
1·6– 3·3	2	24·5	
3·4– 5·4	3	27·4	Moderate Breeze
5·5– 7·9	4	20·3	Moderate Breeze
8·0–10·7	5	4·1	Strong Breeze
10·8–13·8	6 and 7	1·0	Strong Breeze to Moderate Gale
13·9–17·1	8 onwards	0·1	Fresh Gale, etc.

when the English windmills could work effectively was much more limited than their Dutch counterparts.

In England there was another disadvantage, for the windmill usually pumped into either a river that was liable to flood, or into the sea which rose and fell with the tides. In either case there were likely to be periods when the water outside the mill had reached a level higher than the windmill was able to pump. In Holland most areas did not have the same difficulty with river floods, and the tidal problem was overcome by building storage lakes into which windmills could pump all the time and from which the water was run into the sea through self-acting sluices at convenient stages of the tide. Some of these storage lakes were constructed in England, but they were never very common. The tide in the Wash might rise to 15 feet, but a windmill could raise water only about 5 feet. When the tide was favourable, there might not be enough wind, or the wind might come when the tide was up and in this case "the engines must be gentle spectators till the Sea gives way".[40] High floods in the rivers would also prevent the windmills working, even with a good wind, and sometimes stopped the steam-engines (e.g. the Stretham engine in 1852).[41] One of the more important reasons for improving the mouth of the Ouse by digging the Eau Brink Cut was that the floods would escape more quickly and there would be less "head" for the mills to work against. Lowering a high flood by 2 feet might enable the mills to work and would relieve the pressure on the banks. In 1791 a loss of only 2 inches of water against several districts during a winter flood was "looked upon as auspicious, and was testified by visible signs of joy in the countenance of many worthy and industrious farmers".[42]

The position was further aggravated by the subsidence of the land-level through better drainage, although this could be countered by using "double-lift" mills. One mill pumped the water from the land into a storage basin from which a second mill pumped it into the river. The basin between the mills would be from 50 to 100 yards long and 10 to 20 yards wide, lined with clay to prevent the water soaking back through the peat. In this way, water could be raised 8 to 10 feet, and in Holland this system was more fully developed, "it being common . . . to see three or four Windmills playing from one to another, so that the water is raised over a Bank sometimes twelve or fourteen Feet in Height perpendicular".[43] This idea had been known for a long while in England[44] and had to be applied with increasing frequency. The Littleport and Downham drainage area built a double-lift mill in 1812 to work in conjunction with their old Wey Next mill[45] and the Waterbeach Level installed an "inner mill" to lift water to their existing Dollard mill in 1814.[46] Sometimes there was a double-lift system in disguise, for example in the Waldersea and Deeping

"Triple-Lift" mills of the Rijnland Drainage Board, Holland

Fen districts, where the individual farmer each had his own smaller mill to lift water from his land into the main drain while the drainage authorities maintained larger mills to pump the water out of the main drains into the river. Some of these smaller mills remained after steam-engines had been introduced.

The inadequacy of the mills stimulated technical inventions to improve their performance. Although the modifications with spring sails and fantails do not seem to have been used in the Fens, a Dutch patent form of scoopwheel was tried. Mr Eckhardt aimed to reduce the loss of power in a scoopwheel when the ladle first hits the water and when it lifts the water too high at the outlet. He tilted the scoopwheel on to its side at an angle of about forty degrees[47] so that the ladles entered and left the water more smoothly. He also improved the bearings of the scoopwheel, using metal lubricated with oil instead of stone blocks and grease. Eckhardt took out a patent in England, and a certain number of his mills were built in the Fens, perhaps one in Deeping Fen but certainly one near Wisbech[48] and one on the Witham erected by Mr Chaplin of Blankney.[49] Accounts of the performance of these mills vary – "Mr Weston who built it, assured me that it is unquestionably superior to the vertical; but that the millwrights of the country, who cannot execute them well, are averse to the use, and will not let them have fair play if concerned."[50] The invention was fully investigated in Holland,[51] but in spite of the claims of superiority, this type never became popular and none remain even in that country.

Until modern research into aerodynamics improved the shape of windmill sails by streamlining the stocks, the windmill had been developed as far as was possible. Even so, the land was kept in little better than a half-drained state.[52] Money had been spent on drainage schemes that looked well when written as an Act of Parliament, but were "vain

34

and nugatory".[53] The burden of taxes was immense, in fact "a Windmill drainage is the most imperfect of all modes and in many cases the adoption of such a mode may be said to be a useless waste of money".[54] It was only the natural fertility of the land that in one good year would recompense the farmer for the care and hazard of many bad ones that kept the fenland farmers fighting against the floods.[55]

NOTES

1. N. Kinderley, *The Ancient and Present State of the Navigation of . . . Lyn . . .* (1751), p. 13.
2. R. Mylne, *Report . . . on the Proposed Improvement of . . . the River Ouse* (1792), p. 19.
3. J. Rennie, Letter Books, vol. 1, p. 84, 16 February 1789.
   The Navigation from Mildenhall (the Lark) is in a very indifferent state.
   ibid., vol. 11, p. 216, 19 July 1820.
   The Hundred Foot River is throughout its whole length too shallow for the purpose either of discharging the flood water brought down by the Ouse from the interior country or for the Drainage of the Low Lands lying on each side of it.
4. R. Mylne, op. cit., pp. 22 and 48.
5. J. Rennie, Letter Books, vol. 2, p. 428, 1 December 1802.
6. ibid., p. 439, 26 October 1803.
7. W. H. Wheeler, *The History of the Fens of South Lincolnshire* (2nd ed. 1897), p. 298.
8. J. Rennie, Letter Books, vol. 2, p. 376, 6 October 1800.
9. N. Walker and T. Craddock, *The History of Wisbech and the Fens* (1849), p. 440.
10. J. Rennie, Letter Books, vol. 7, p. 413, 26 January 1814.
    It is therefore evident that the great bar to the discharge of the waters of the Nene and of course to the general Drainage of the Lands depending on this river is the high and shifting sands which lie between Gunthorpe Sluice and Crabhole, and the narrow and confined channel through the town of Wisbech. If the outfall of the Nene is to be effectually improved, it must be by a new channel from the mouth of Kinderley's Cut at Gunthorpe Sluice to the level of low water in the Bay at some place or other.
11. W. Richards, *The History of Lynn* (1812), p. 27.
12. S. Wells, *The History of the Drainage of . . . Bedford Level* (1830), vol. I, p. 755.
13. J. Rennie, Letter Books, vol. 1, p. 86, 16 February 1789.
14. *Observations on the means of better draining the Middle and South Levels of the Fens, by two gentlemen who have taken a view thereof* (1777).
    A few miles above the town at a part called Germans, the River is very wide, in some places it is more than half a mile across, where the water is shallow, there being Barrs of Sand formed that hold it back upon the Country, which are occasioned by the too-great width of the River, as the necessary Velocity of the stream to preserve its proper depth is thereby lost.
15. A. Young, *A. of A.*, vol. 43, p. 543.
16. ibid., p. 551, and also vol. 44, pp. 43 and 284; W. Gooch, *Cambridge* (1813), p. 210; J. Rennie, *Report on . . . the South and Middle Levels . . .* (1809).
17. T. Stone, *Huntingdon* (1793), p. 31.
    Persons interested in the navigation of the port of Lynn to the sea, are said to oppose this intended cut, upon the ground, that the rapidity with which the water will come from the highland, thus confined or circumscribed in its bounds, will not only increase the existing defects in the harbour (these being sand-banks below the port of Lynn, which are immoveable, and on that account, sediment there will be increased), but that it will endanger that part of the town. Arguements supposed to be destructive of each other, for the same power which would endanger the town of Lynn, would not fail, in a proper direction to clear its way through no small impediments, to the sea.
18. T. Neale, *The Ruinous State of the parish of Manea . . .* (1748), p. 14. D. Defoe, *A Tour through the whole Island of Great Britain* (1724), vol. II, p. 151.
19. C. T. G. Boucher, *John Rennie . . .* (1963), p. 2.
20. L. Gibbs, "Pumping Machinery . . .", *Min. Inst. Civ. Eng.*, vol. XCIV (1888), p. 266.
21. F. Stokhuyzen, *The Dutch Windmill* (1962), p. 37.
22. P. Bateson, *An Answer to some Objections of Hatton Berners Esq.* (1710), p. 10.
23. Ely Diocesan Records, Haddenham Level Account Books, 1739–41 and 1743–5.
24. A. Young, *Lincoln* (1799), p. 240, and J. A. Clarke, *J.R.A.S.*, vol. 48 (1848), p. 102.
25. Lansdowne MS., 41/46 (1584).
26. 53 Geo. III, L. & P., c. 81.

27. Waterbeach Level Account Book, 1815–16, also W. Gooch, *Cambridge* (1813), p. 67, for a windmill costing £1,400 at Wilmington, and A. Young, *A. of A.*, vol. 44, p. 278, for two at Wisbech costing £1,200 each, vol. 16, p. 464, for mills costing £600 in Burnt Fen and vol. 36, p. 90, for small mills costing £80.

28. R. Parkinson, *Huntingdon* (1813), p. 21. C. Labelye, *Result of a View of the Great Level of the Fens . . .* (1745), p. 55.

29. J. Rennie, Letter Books, vol. 11, p. 342, 6 December 1820.

30. G. D. Dempsey, *Rudimentary Treatise on the Drainage of Districts and Lands* (1854), p. 12.

31. B. and W. Coll., R. Wild to J. Watt, 28 November 1789.

32. Lansdowne MS., 46/56, p. 113.

33. P. Bateson, op. cit., p. 10.

34. B. and W. Coll., J. Watt to W. Swansborough, 6 August 1814.

35. J. Nickalls, *Report . . . upon the New Cut from Eau-Brink . . .* (1793), p. 4.

36. B. and W. Coll., J. Watt to W. Swansborough, 6 August 1814.

37. ibid., 18 August 1814.

38. F. Stokhuyzen, op. cit., pp. 95–6.

39. ibid., p. 97.

40. P. Bateson, op. cit., p. 10.

41. Waterbeach Level Records, Report on Flood, February 1900.

42. J. Golborne, *The Report of James Golborne of the City of Ely, Engineer* (1791), p. 33.

43. C. Labelye, op. cit., p. 15.

44. W. Dodson, *The Designe . . .* (1665), p. 23.

45. Littleport and Downham District Minutes, 13 October 1812. Other double-lift mills mentioned in these Minutes are Littleport, 31 October 1827, and Westmoor, 27 November 1828.

46. Waterbeach Level Order Book, 27 May 1814.

47. A Young, *Lincoln* (1799), p. 240.

48. A. Young, *A. of A.*, vol. 44, p. 278.

49. A. Young, *Lincoln* (1799), p. 240.

50. A. Young, *A. of A.*, vol. 44, p. 278.

51. ibid., vol. 26, pp. 388 ff.

52. J. Rennie, Letter Books, vol. 7, p. 412, 28 January 1813.

53. A. Young, *A. of A.*, vol. 43, p. 543.

54. J. Rennie, Letter Books, vol. 11, p. 340, 6 December 1820.

55. G. Maxwell, *Huntingdon* (1793), p. 24.

CHAPTER IV

The Convertible System

The Fens provided a livelihood for many people even before any attempts at drainage had been made. In the rivers and open waters there were fish and eels, and some of the monasteries had to pay taxes in the form of the latter. Fishing is still a very popular pastime beside the rivers, but luckily catching eels with the eel-gleave has died out. This was like a fork with a long wooden handle tipped with three or four broad iron prongs having sharp barbs that stuck into the eel as the gleave was prodded into the mud. In the middle of the eighteenth century, a group of Cambridge undergraduates founded the Upware Republic, based on the inn the "Five Miles from Anywhere – No Hurry" at Upware, to go shooting wildfowl in the Fens, for game-birds of all sorts from geese to small waders abounded everywhere, and decoys were built to catch ducks. The fenmen have many good tales to tell, and Defoe went away happily believing that special ducks were trained to go and tell their companions in foreign parts, using some form of duckey language, about the good feeding that the Fens provided. These birds would bring their friends to the ponds where the decoys were concealed and lead them up the channels under the nets to where the wildfowler was waiting to catch and kill them. The trained ducks were set free to go and fetch more. Even if the details are a little fanciful, the decoy-ponds attracted many birds, and in the season cartloads of ducks were sent off to London and other places. These decoys were often worked by the Fen Slodgers, a race of men who lived in the Fens entirely upon the natural resources of the area, the last of whom died within living memory.

On the silt lands in the north, the fine medieval churches show how prosperous these lands have been and the pattern of fairly dense settlement is far different from the empty black peat areas to the south. All the villages surrounding the Fens had common rights over the peat lands which provided many necessities for their livelihood. Besides fish and fowl, the wetter parts grew reeds for thatching. Norfolk reeds are still famous, but, although this crop paid well, it was found more profitable in the Fens to drain the land wherever possible for cultivation.[1] Also there was sedge which was cut and dried for either thatching or burning. It was sent by water to places up-country for the purpose of drying malt[2] or used for fuel by many of the poorer people. Another crop was osiers, and there were willows for making eel and fish traps or baskets.

More important than any of these products was turf, or peat, cut and dried for fuel. This was much cheaper than coal, and often preferred in Cambridge and many of the towns around the Fens because it had no nasty smell, did not make as much soot, and would smoulder away night and day with very little attention. Turf-cutting seems to have been more strictly regulated in the Fens than in Norfolk or Holland. The Norfolk Broads were formed by peat-cutting before 1500,[3] and parts of Holland were denuded in the same way during the sixteenth and seventeenth centuries for peat fuel. In the Fens, the loose sedge and reeds would be cleared away until solid peat was reached. Then the turf would be dug out with a special two-edged spade called a becket. Once the first row had been removed, a single stroke of the becket cut a fresh slice free which would be placed on a barrow to be carried away to a stack for drying. Balks were left between the trenches and dug out a few years later when the trenches had grown over and were beginning to fill up again with rotting vegetation. In this way the level of the land was not drastically reduced, although it took a few years before the peat grew again to its former level. In some areas there was trouble with flooding on peat land where turf had been cut, and in 1732 the Bedford Level Corporation ordered that, on the Adventurers lands, "no person be admitted to cut any turf but for their own burning".[4] The Waterbeach Level first restricted the areas in which peat was cut and finally by the Enclosure Act of 1813[5] forbade cutting altogether. Wicken Fen has never been enclosed and all these forms of activity survived there until the 1930s.

The drier parts of the peat districts supported sheep and cattle, usually only in the summer when the water had drained away. The numbers allowed on the commons were closely regulated, but the pasture was often poor and full of reeds. The silt lands were predominantly pasture that was of good quality and cattle were sent there from the highlands to be fattened before going on to London for slaughtering. But in all of these areas, conditions might change completely over the course of a few years. Where Defoe had seen only floods, a few years later in 1745 Labelye (a native of Switzerland who designed and built the first Westminster Bridge) could ride and hardly wet his horse's hooves even in the rivers when he was surveying the Fens.[6] In 1799 Arthur Young wrote about Deeping Fen that it "is a very capital improvement by draining. Twenty years ago the lands sold for about £3 an acre; some was then let at 7s. or 8s. an acre; and a great deal was in such a state that nobody would rent it; now it is in general worth 20s. an acre and sells at £20 an acre."[7] But the drainage must have deteriorated again, for it was reported in 1818 that the whole Fen was "in a lost state".[8]

Early in 1805, Arthur Young made another visit to the Cambridgeshire Fens and found he had to alter his previous impression

that the tracts which could be properly classed as waste land, were not of very considerable extent, but the journey I have made convinced me of the contrary; and the whole appeared to be in such manifest danger of inundation, that I could not but agree in the propriety of being particular in the examination I took of this interesting country.[9]

On his travels he went to the house of a labourer William Fletcher that presented a "spectacle of wretchedness not often to be met with".[10] During the summer of 1799 this man with his wife and three children had spent only one month downstairs and during the following winter the water was two feet deep on their ground-floor. Even in the next July they still had to use a boat to go to and fro. In another area, where Casaubon had travelled, Young met Talbot who with his wife and four children lived in a hut he had built in Downham Fen. He laboured at cutting sedge and turf and fishing, but the floods increased until he was forced to abandon his hut and move to the town of Downham.

The fenmen may have become immune to this sort of insecurity, but it came as a shock to strangers. A foreigner to the Fens, Mr Cole, purchased some land in the Waterbeach district

great part of which has been drowned these two years and is now getting dry again. . . . On Monday night the bank of the river blew up, and has overflown a vast tract of country in this neighbourhood. I was all day yesterday on the water to see their operations; but they will hardly be able to stop it in three or four days. The mischief was occasioned by the rain on Sunday last. . . . All this part of the country is now covered with water, and the poor people of this parish utterly ruined. I am determined to sell my estate in this country. Every shower puts me on the rack, and I have suffered exceedingly these four or five years.[11]

Conditions did not improve, for in the following year there were more floods, and this time his estate was drowned worse than ever.[12] Cole finally sold his estate for one wet season followed another, "but never so bad as last November's floods, which totally drowned all our country, and when it will be dry again, God knows. . . . Thank God I have got rid of this plague and anxiety by parting with my estate, which instead of being service, was a continual uneasiness to me, and of no great advantage."[13]

Yet some farmers welcomed the floods, for the nature of the soil was such that the lands would have been of little value without something to enrich the soil and bind it together. When the floods had subsided and the land had dried out, plentiful crops could be produced.[14] These methods may not have mattered much under the old farming techniques, but, as farming became more intensive and absorbed greater capital following the agricultural improvements especially associated with Norfolk, better drainage became a necessity if progress were to be maintained. On the whole the villagers found an adequate though uncertain living from their commons. There was free fuel which they had only to collect and from which they could make a little cash by selling in the near-by towns.[15] Reeds, sedge, fish and fowl helped to supplement their income or provide a more varied diet, while they could also keep a few sheep or cows and, if the year was very dry, they might cultivate part of the common land. For this sort of person, better drainage was opposed to their own interests and they were loath to surrender their rights. As long as the land was held commonly, it could not be developed profitably, and overstocked common land did not provide enough return to pay the increased taxes that were necessary for better drainage. Moreover, the average commoner did not have enough capital to drain his allotment when it was enclosed.

While it was difficult enough to find agreement among the commoners of one small area, in some parts various towns shared rights over the same fen. Among the most notorious examples of this "inter-commoning" were the East, West and Wildmore Fens near Boston

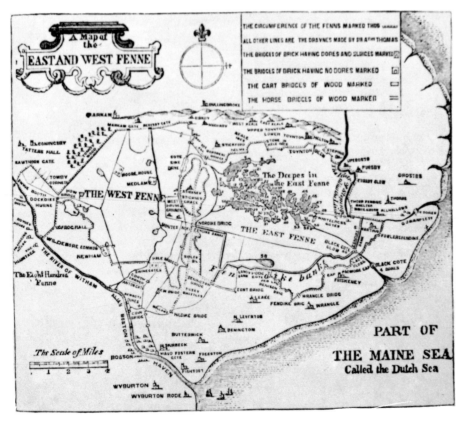

Map of East, West and Wildmore Fens; from S. Smiles, Lives of the Engineers

containing in the whole about 40,000 acres; here are depastured very small and lean cattle, horses and sheep, with a multitude of geese which are kept chiefly for their feathers, being plucked three or four times in a year; to most of these animals, a hard winter or the rot is very apt to be fatal. A small part of the fen is covered with water, and furnishes a very few fish, and not many wild-fowl. . . . Twenty two towns in parts of Lindsey and eight towns in parts of Holland have undisputed rights of common in West Fen. . . . The twenty two towns have the same rights in East Fen, the eight towns claim rights of pasturage here. . . . Seventeen towns of Lindsey and one of Holland have rights in Wildmore Fen.[16]

In the East Fen there was a chain of lakes surrounded by great crops of reeds, for Arthur Young was taken through this part in a boat.[17] In the other parts the drainage was un-certain, so that whatever might be gained in one or two years was liable to be all lost in the next.[18] Although there were regulations about stocking the pastures, in good years the temptation to make a quick profit was too great and too much stock was turned on to the land so the pastures were overgrazed and ruined.[19] This "horrible collection of waters in the Fens . . . which at present yield us little else than pestilential air, rotten sheep, starved geese, and stunted cattle – instead of grain and meat in glorious abundance"[20] had too long been a scandal to the country.

Sir Joseph Banks owned part of these Fens and he provided the driving force necessary to carry out a scheme of drainage. There was great opposition, partly from the poorer people who would lose their common rights, but others thought that the plans proposed by John Rennie were impracticable.[21] For example, a "Holland Watchman" asked about the East Fen:

What does Mr. Rennie promise you? Does he say, that your lands shall be as well drained in all seasons, as Wildmore and the West Fens? No! Does he say, that even in summer they shall never be suddenly drowned? He does not even undertake that. What then does he hold forth to you? I will *sift* his words: and leave you to judge, whether, like the wheat of the late unfortunate harvest, they do not consist of much bran, and little or no good flour.[22]

All these three Fens were drained by Rennie's scheme entirely by gravitation and without the use of any wind- or steam-engines. The report of Anthony Bower in 1814 illustrates the great change that had been effected:

Before any works were undertaken in the year 1799 . . . the low lands and commons adjoining . . . were under water except for a small part in Wildmore and West Fen. . . . The lower part of West Fen . . . and the lower part of Wildmore Fen were under water every winter . . . the East Fen deeps were always under water during the summer. . . . It is a pleasure to state that every wished for object in the drainage of the whole of the Fens and low lands adjoining is obtained and the lowest land brought into a state of safe cultivation. The East Fen deeps are so perfectly drained, and so confident are the proprietors of this that part of them now forms a considerable farmyard.[23]

The East, West and Wildmore Fens were mainly silt lands, and were one of the last areas of this type that had not been improved previously in any way. The greater part of the silt lands had been improved and enclosed during the 1780s[24] or in the following decade. Before 1800, grazing still remained the principal occupation and there was not much plough-land nor had the low Fens come into general cultivation. The high prices of corn during the Napoleonic Wars caused a general ploughing of the grazing land[25] that turned into an attempt to bring into cultivation the waste peat lands throughout the Fens. In Cambridgeshire, in 1794, there were 50,000 acres of improved fen and 150,000 acres of waste or unimproved fen, while by 1806 a further 20,000 acres had been improved.[26] In

Huntingdonshire, there were 8,000 or 10,000 productive acres out of a total 44,000 acres of fen in 1793 and in 1813 there were 32,000 acres of improved fen.[27]

In their waste and unimproved state, the Fens were worth an average of 4s. per acre per annum.[28] Burwell Fen was valued at only 1s. per acre,[29] while Great Wilbraham Fen, before it was enclosed in 1797, was let at 2s. 6d. per acre.[30] If there were prospects that the drainage would be improved, the price of land increased enormously. Some land which had been valued at between £4 and £10 an acre increased to between £20 and £30.[31] On those lands that could be adequately drained, the rents averaged 20s. to 25s. per acre. Silt land, where the drainage was more certain, fetched more.[32] Enclosures and new Acts to improve the drainage helped to raise rents. An Act was passed for the areas of Marshland Smeeth and Marshland Fen, for the drainage of the Fen and the division and allotment of both. Afterwards, part of the Smeeth which was silt land was sold for £50 an acre and would let at £3 an acre while the Fen let at only 25s. an acre.

This great tract of land was in its former state worth little: the Fen not above 1/– an acre in reed, being two or three feet deep under water; the Smeeth was often under water, in parts to the amount of half, and then at the mid-summer after rotted the sheep that fed it. Above 30,000 £ a year is added to the produce of the kingdom by this most beneficial undertaking.[33]

Area	Acres	Improved Value		Old Value		Improvement		Expenditure
		£	s.	£	s.	£	s.	£
Anwick Fen	1,097	703	16	54	17	648	19	4,070
The Nine Embanked Fens from Tattershall to Lincoln	19,418	15,534	8	1,941	16	13,592	12	77,672
Holland Fen Eleven Towns	22,000	25,300	0	3,600	0	21,700	0	50,600
Tattershall Embankment	892	838	0	387	0	450	0	not given
	43,407	42,375	0	5,982	0	36,390	0	[34]

On these improved silt areas, quite a wide variety of crops was grown. In the parishes of Upwell, Welney, Outwell, Elme and Wisbech hemp and flax were planted. The cultivation of these was stimulated mainly by the high import taxes imposed during the Napoleonic Wars, for it ceased once the duties were removed in 1832.[35] Mention might also be made of woad, which continued to be grown near Wisbech until the early twentieth century, but these crops were very small and never of great importance.

The type of farming that was practised on the newly enclosed and drained peat lands was called by Gooch "The Convertible System".[36] The methods had been employed in the Fens for many years previously on a small scale,[37] but during the Napoleonic Wars their use became much more general. Peat, by itself, is of little use as arable land. It is too light, and easily blows away when dry. The particles of old vegetation of which it consists do not readily form a compact soil, so that the roots of the crops are not embedded firmly enough to gain sufficient nourishment. In addition, the acid which has preserved the peat injures anything that is grown in it. Therefore before it can be turned into good arable, this acid must be neutralized and the tilth made more compact. However, should the water be allowed to rise in the fen, the water that still remains in the lower part of the peat will rise and destroy the good effects of whatever methods have been used to counteract the acid. Therefore it was not worth while spending great sums of money on improving the peat land until a proper drainage could be guaranteed, but the peat itself provided a temporary remedy which formed the basis of agriculture in these areas until the advent of better drainage.

About one-third of those peat lands that were not reserved for permanent pasture were ploughed in each year and the remainder kept under grass. Before any arable cultivation was attempted, the first thing that was done was to pare (or lightly plough) the surface, and then burn it. A special plough was used to break up the grass, and when the sods were sufficiently dry, the furrows or parings were placed in heaps and burnt. The resulting ashes were spread over the land, which helped to put out the fire and prevented it burning too deeply. There was always the danger with paring and burning that in very dry seasons, when "the moisture of the earth is very low, the fire catches the soil below and causes what is called *pitting*, making great unsightly holes to the bottom of the moor which with great difficulty are extinguished. About thirteen years ago, a large common at Chatteris in the Isle of Ely, was thus burnt up, 16 or 18 inches deep to the very gravel."[38] Also when the banks were made from peat, there was danger that the fire would destroy them unless great care were taken.[39] The alkali in the ashes helped to counteract the acid in the peat, and the resulting tilth produced good crops, but the effects soon wore off.

There were great arguments as to the advisability of paring and burning, for it was claimed by many that the peat was wasted and the surface drastically lowered. In evidence of this, Thomas Stone wrote:

Upon the old ploughed land in the neighbourhood of these commons, which have been repeatedly pared and burnt, the ploughs frequently take hold of wood, and the roots of trees, where they had always uninterruptedly gone before, at equal depth from the surface, during the memory of man; which is of sufficient proof that paring and burning reduces the soil; and such adjacent ploughed land which was considered higher than the commons when first inclosed, is now 18 inches lower, which is entirely occasioned by paring and burning.[40]

Others suggested that it was not the level of the arable land that sank, but "that the surface of the adjacent depastured fen lands, from the decay of vegetables, dung of animals, and the soil brought thither by the waters from neighbouring high lands, has been continually though slowly increasing".[41] From the fact that ordinary soils cannot be wasted by burning, the lowering of the fenlands was attributed to the consolidation of the particles.[42] But since peat is almost entirely vegetable matter, the practice of burning must have helped to lower the level of the land. Whatever arguments were produced for or against it, it was the cheapest and some considered the only effective way to cultivate the Fens and so this method continued.[43]

After paring and burning, it was always the practice to sow cole or rape.[44] The cole, if it were not left for seed to make Colza oil, was fed off while still green by sheep. The sheep helped to make the soil more compact by trampling upon it, for it was often too soft after the first ploughing for horses to work on it.[45] After cole, oats almost invariably followed, and the early practice was to continue sowing oats or other white grain as long as the land would continue to produce a crop, and then allow it to remain two or three years "producing every kind of beggary; then the process of burnbaking is again performed".[46] Other less exhausting systems of rotation were evolved, sometimes wheat or beans or clover being sown with an occasional year of seeds or grass to give the land a rest.[47] Mr Saffory, who had fen farms at Denver, Welney, Fordham and Downham, used the following course. "First, pare and burn, cole for sheep, crop worth 30/– to 40/–. Second, oats, 15 coombs. Third, wheat, 7 coombs. Fourth, summerland cole for sheep, 25/– and fifth, oats, 15 coombs."[48] Various farmers tried out experiments with different crops and rotations so that there was no system generally pursued except beginning with paring and burning. Then followed cole and oats until the first luxuriance of the soil had abated and the tilth had acquired more consistency when other crops such as wheat might be tried.[49]

With all these systems of management, besides that part which was never ploughed, it was still necessary to have only one-third of the remainder under arable and two-thirds in grass.[50] This was to enable the vegetation to rot and built up the peat again so that it was not completely worn away by repeated paring and burning. If the farmers had not practised this lying in grass, the peat would have soon disappeared or sunk so low that drainage would have become impossible. Arthur Young shows how little fenland was used for arable. From the total area of fen, 300,000 acres, he deducted 6,000 acres for meres, and 4 acres in every 100 acres, or 12,000 acres, for ditches etc., leaving for agricultural use say 280,000 acres. This he divided as follows:

Acres		Value
28,000	Cole, fed at 30s.	£ 42,000
28,000	Wheat, 3½ quarters, 98,000 at 50s.	245,000
56,000	Oats, 6 quarters at 20s.	336,000
168,000	Grass at 20s.	168,000
		£791,000

This is in its very imperfect drainage, which injures the grass greatly, and reduces the quantity of wheat considerably through apprehensions of floods.[51]

Although there was the ever-present threat of floods, the produce gathered in a good year would amply repay two or three bad years.[52] The uncertainty of the drainage caused the farmers to concentrate mostly on oats, with the result that "the produce of the fens, when dry, is so great and so much exceeding any other lands, that the growth of oats here governs in some measure the London markets, and consequently has an influence on the whole kingdom".[53] The dependence of the farmers upon oats was so great that in the difficult times after the Napoleonic Wars, the Bedford Level Corporation made strong representations to Parliament not to reduce the import price for oats.[54] The wheat that grew on peat soils was usually poor, being "thicker skinned, and of inferior quality to the highland wheat".[55] It also tended to produce too much straw so it often fell down and could not be harvested. However, when there were no floods and the crops hit, the produce, especially of oats, was much above average for the whole country. Vancouver gives as the produce per acre in the Fens "32 bushels of Wheat, weighing fifty five pounds per bushel, and 42 bushels of oats, weighing thirty two pounds per bushel".[56] The following table is compiled from various figures given in his book and other writers also commented on the greater productivity of the Fens compared with the highlands.[57]

	Wheat	Barley	Oats (Bushels)
General average	23·3	36·1	26·2
Open fields and waste land	20·2	21·0	25·1
Fenland	24·4	29·6	47·0

Although the fen grounds were richer and more fertile than anywhere else in the kingdom, the land was more subject to blights than in the hilly parts and the grain lighter and of inferior quality.[58] The fen farmers tried to make up in quantity what they lacked in quality and so resorted to various devices.

In the vicinity of Market Deeping, the arable common fields are ploughed up into broad arched lands, the furrows for three, four, or five yards wide, laid down to grass and mown for hay, while

43

the crowns of the ridges are under grass. This management is excellent, and much superior to having such miserable corn in these furrows, from wetness, as is seen from Chattris towards Whittlesea to Peterborough; the centres of the lands being high, are dry and fit for corn, and the furrows low, do well for grass.[59]

Such methods show that the existing drainage was inadequate. With windmills, the drainage was uncertain, but it was expensive to make any improvements so that often the Fens were in too wet a state for cultivation. In bad years many farmers could not afford to pay their drainage taxes so that considerable areas were frequently forfeited to the Bedford Level Corporation. Often the taxes charged upon the land far exceeded any profits that the occupiers could hope to gain, and so they preferred to relinquish their estates rather than pay the taxes imposed upon them.[60] This made it difficult for the Bedford Level Corporation to remain solvent, and the same thing was happening to the smaller drainage authorities. The Waterbeach Level Account Book shows a gradually increasing deficit from non-payment of taxes, and there are frequent complaints in the Order Book with injunctions for seizure and sale of land.

Some people saw that in order to have really efficient fen farming, it was necessary to drain deeper, and to remove the soak or "subterranean water" which lay but a few feet from the surface.[61] This soak is cold water full of acid. The roots of the crops stop growing once they reach it, and if it should rise above the roots, then the plants are seriously retarded or even killed. If the soak should actually rise to the surface, then all the good effects of paring and burning are lost and the cycle has to be started from the beginning again. The sooner the water could be removed from the land and the soak lowered after the winter, the sooner the farmer could start his sowing. "Hence it is obvious that the lower the land is situated, the later must be the seed time."[62] Therefore a few people suggested developing the windmill drainage further. At this time the mills were only used to relieve the surface water, but if they could be employed to keep the soak a sufficient depth below the surface, then the seed time could be advanced and fewer crops would be lost.

Yet the windmills were not able to guarantee an adequate drainage even for the standards of those days, and, so long as reliance was placed upon them, there was always the danger that all would be lost through floods. The work of many years reclamation could easily be undone in a single bad year, as Arthur Young vividly shows.

In 1799, above 25,000 acres were under water till May 1800, to the south of the Hundred-foot drain, and all much annoyed by the flood; and it was a melancholy examination I took of the country between Whittlesea and March in the middle of July, in all which tract of ten miles, usually under great crops of cole, oats, and wheat, there was nothing to be seen but desolation, with here and there a crop of oats or barley, sown so late that they came to nothing: a great loss by seeding the land at so high a price. Some crops on the rather higher spots, looked well, but very late. Of wheat there is not an acre. The grass itself is very much damaged; produces where mown, miserable crops of sedge instead of good grasses; and where fed, keeping very little stock, and that badly. Yet the average rent of these ten miles is 14s. an acre; and the landlord has a heavy drainage tax to pay of 5s. an acre, and in some districts 7s. sunk for security, but repaid by inundation.[63]

Some areas were high enough to be drained with very little trouble,[64] but this could not be done for most of the Fens. Much had been done to improve the drains, and after the Napoleonic Wars improvements were made in the main rivers so that the flood water flowed more quickly to the sea. In 1820 the lower lying areas of the Fens still waited for a complete and effectual draining before it was possible to restore "a tract of far more fruitful, and productive land than is to be met with of the like extent in any part of the island".[65] Although the lands had been improved enormously since the turn of the century, the full potential had not yet been discovered, for less than half was under the plough, and the old system of paring and burning followed by mostly oats was still in use. The reports made to the Select Committee of the House of Commons investigating the depressed state of agriculture in 1821 show what the Fens were like before revolutionary changes occurred in the next two decades. Mr Thomas Orton, who lived at Ely and was a Conservator of the Bedford Level, was asked to give evidence.

Will you state to the Committee, what proportion of land in the Fens, you suppose is generally sown with oats? – The general system in the Fens, is one-third corn, and probably one-fifth, or rather more than one-fifth would be oats. I have no doubt that the Fens are now growing two-fifths corn, and one-fifth of which is oats.

What is generally the quality of land in the Isle of Ely? – They vary very materially; there are some very fine lands, and some very inferior, but all are productive lands if well drained.

Have you much grazing land in your part of the country? – There is a considerable deal of grazing land; I cannot tell what the proportion may be.

You have said nothing about wheat? – We are not much of a wheat country. . . . Our soils are much more congenial to the growth of oats than wheat. . . .

What course do you adopt? – We are very irregular in our mode of cultivation; we grow about two-fifths corn, the other cole or turnips and grass.[66]

It was very much more profitable for the farmer to grow wheat instead of oats, but this could only be done if the drainage were reasonably secure. The gains to be expected from an adequate drainage were very great. No longer would the sowing of crops be delayed through the wetness of the soil and there would be no danger of losing the seed or the crops if there should be a heavy rain that caused the soak to rise. Also the evil of twitch grass, that in a wet season smothered everything, would be abated. There were positive advantages to be gained as well. The soil would progressively improve and there would be no danger of ruin through uncertain drainage. The best practices of husbandry could safely be adopted without fear of losing the whole. "The lands will remain longer in grass, their herbage will be more valuable, and when they are ploughed, the corn will be superior in quality."[67]

NOTES

1. W. Gooch, *Cambridge* (1811), p. 111.
2. C. Vancouver, *Cambridge* (1794), p. 36.
3. J. M. Lambert, *The Making of the Broads*, R.G.S. Series (1960).
4. B.L.C., London, 30 May 1732.
5. 53 Geo. III, L. & P., c. 107.
6. D. Defoe, *A tour through the whole Island of Great Britain* (1724), vol. I, p. 119. C. Labelye, *Result of a View of the Great Level of the Fens . . .* (1745).
7. A. Young, *Lincoln* (1799), pp. 117 and 235.
8. J. Rennie, Letter Books, vol. 10, p. 5, 16 October 1818.
9. A. Young, *A. of A.*, vol. 43, p. 539.
10. ibid., p. 546.
11. E. Warburton, *Life of Horace Walpole* (1851), Letter from Cole, 21 June 1769.
12. ibid., Letter from Cole, 28 November 1770.
13. ibid., Letter from Cole, 18 April 1771.
14. Harleian MS., 5011, vol. 1, p. 206. W. K. Clay, *History of the Parish of Waterbeach* (1859), p. 17.
15. E. Carter, *History of the County of Cambridge* (1753), p. 16.
16. A. Young, *A. of A.*, vol. 26, Letter from Rev. S. Partridge, 4 April 1796.
17. A. Young, *Lincoln* (1799), p. 232.

18. J. Rennie, Letter Books, vol. 7, p. 433, 23 February 1814.
19. T. Stone, *Lincoln* (1794), p. 15.
20. Sir G. Heathcote, *Thoughts of a Lincolnshire Freeholder* . . . (1794), p. 14.
21. A Holland Watchman, *A Remonstrance against . . . the Report of Mr. John Rennie* . . . (1800).
22. ibid., p. 16.
23. J. Rennie, Letter Books, vol. 7, p. 428, 23 February 1814.
24. See W. H. Wheeler, *The History of the Fens of South Lincolnshire* (2nd ed. 1897).
25. House of Commons, *Minutes of Evidence taken before Select Committee on Agricultural Distress, March 1836*, Questions 7806–7.
26. C. Vancouver; op. cit., p. 1, and W. Gooch, op. cit., p. 2.
27. G. Maxwell, *Huntingdon* (1793), p. 23, and R. Parkinson, *Huntingdon* (1813), p. 174.
28. W. Richards, *The History of Lynn* (1812), vol. I, p. 73.
29. C. Vancouver, op. cit., p. 36.
30. W. Gooch, op. cit., p. 67.
31. A. Young, *A. of A.*, vol. 43, p. 553.
32. A. Young, *Norfolk* (1804), p. 39.
33. ibid., p. 137.
34. A. Young, *Lincoln* (1799), p. 86.
35. D. and S. Lysons, *Cambridgeshire, Magna Britannia* (1808), p. 36.
36. W. Gooch, op. cit., p. 105.
37. W. Blith, *The English Improver Improved* (2nd ed. 1652), pp. 59 ff.
38. A. Young, *Lincoln* (1799), p. 247.
39. 37 Geo. III, L. & P., c. 88, Waterbeach Level Act.
40. T. Stone, op. cit., p. 23.
41. A. Young, *Lincoln* (1799), p. 247.
42. ibid., p. 425.
43. C. Vancouver, op. cit., p. 201.
44. T. Stone, op. cit., p. 15.
45. A. Young, *Norfolk* (1804), p. 137.
46. T. Stone, *Huntingdon* (1793), p. 13.
47. A. Young, *Lincoln* (1799), p. 95.
48. A. Young, *Norfolk* (1804), p. 137.
49. A. Young, *Lincoln* (1799), p. 95.
50. G. Maxwell, *Huntingdon* (1793), p. 24.
51. A. Young, *A. of A.*, vol. 44, p. 282.
52. J. Rennie, Letter Books, vol. 7, p. 433, 23 February 1814.
53. A. Young, *A. of A.*, vol. 43, p. 560.
54. B.L.C., Minute Books, 29 May 1822.
55. C. Vancouver, op. cit., p. 36.
56. ibid., p. 235.
57. D. and S. Lysons, op. cit., p. 36.
58. W. Richards, op. cit., p. 74.
59. A. Young, *Lincoln* (1799), p. 92.
60. T. Stone, *Huntingdon* (1793), p. 13.
61. A. Young, *Lincoln* (1799), p. 235.
62. ibid., p. 235.
63. A. Young, *A. of A.*, vol. 43, p. 543.
64. ibid., p. 51, for Chippenham enclosed in 1791.
65. C. Vancouver, op. cit., p. 202.
66. House of Commons, *Minutes of Evidence . . . on the Depressed State of Agriculture, April 1821*, p. 129.
67. T. Wing, *Considerations on the Principles of Mr. Rennie's Plans for the Drainage of the North level . . .* (1820), p. 12.

CHAPTER V

A Remedy in Water Found

The answer to the need for better drainage was already at hand, for although steam had been used to pump water for over a hundred years, its successful application to land drainage had been long delayed. It is not known whether the earliest steam-engine that had some practical success, the Savery engine, was ever seriously considered for pumping water from fen or marsh land at the time of its manufacture. This engine had no moving parts except for a manually operated steam-valve, for it consisted only of a boiler and a receiver. Steam from the boiler forced water out of the receiver, through a non-return valve, and up a pipe to the required height. When all the water had been driven out of the receiver, the steam from the boiler was shut off and cold water poured over the receiver. Into the vacuum thus formed, water was raised by atmospheric pressure from a reservoir below, through another pipe and clack valve. When the receiver had thus been filled with water again, the cycle was repeated. The inventor, Thomas Savery, was granted a patent for "raising water by the impellant force of fire" in 1698 for a period of fourteen years, but later extended to 1733.[1] He made various improvements to the boiler, and fitted twin receivers so that it would work continuously. However, this engine had no safety features whatsoever, and although it could raise water by vacuum about 20 feet, the height to which it could raise water by steam pressure was limited to a further 20 feet owing to the weakness of the materials available. The pressure needed to force water to any greater height was liable to cause the boilers to burst and the soldered joints to melt. Although for land drainage the pressure would not need to be very high, these engines consumed vast quantities of coal. In any case,

Windmills and a steam-engine,
Reedham, Norfolk Broads
(R.H.C.)

for draining Fenlands, Savery's engine was not well adapted; because, in most cases, the water is required to be raised only to a small height, but in very great quantities; several engines would be wanted for one drainage, and a great part of their power would be lost, because the perpendicular height at which the water would be discharged, would always be less than the height to which atmospheric pressure can raise the water.[2]

The first really practical steam-engine was the Newcomen engine. This was fully developed by 1712 to pump water out of mines, and formed the basis of certain steam-engine designs until the closing years of the nineteenth century. It consisted of two vertical cylinders, inside which were pistons, attached by chains to each end of a horizontal wooden beam pivoted in the middle. The cylinder that was placed in the mine shaft was used as a pump with the piston in it lifting the water out of the mine. Later, to give increased lift, two or three sets of pumps might be used, one above the other, but all worked by the same engine. The other cylinder was placed above a boiler so it could be filled with steam. The weight of the pump rods in the mine shaft pulled the pumps down and the other piston up to the top of the steam-cylinder. Cold water was injected into the steam-cylinder so that the atmospheric pressure forced down that piston into the resulting vacuum. This caused the pumps in the mine to be raised and the water to be lifted out. Since the power was supplied by the atmosphere and not by steam pressure, it was very difficult to vary the power of these machines except by altering the diameter of the cylinder. Yet it was a far more economical machine than the Savery engine and had a greater potential for land drainage.

Marten Triewald, a Swedish engineer who came to England in 1716 at the age of twenty-five and helped with the erection of some Newcomen engines, said that

The fire-engine can also be applied to all kinds of mills, e.g. grain- and saw-mills, in shipbuilding yards, and in fortresses, and generally in all places where there are no waterfalls. Item, in mining districts to supply blast furnaces where there is plenty of wood and iron but no waterfall; equally to forges or tilt hammers. Boggy and marshy countries could be drained by quite a small fire-machine, whilst on the other hand dry countries could be irrigated.[3]

When these early fire-engines were applied to "all kinds of mills", they would pump the water into a reservoir from where it would be drawn off to work a waterwheel which turned the machinery, for it was not until 1782 that James Watt developed a successful rotative engine.

Many engineers, among them John Smeaton, thought that steam would one day drain the Fens,[4] but the first steam-engine to have been used solely for land drainage was probably a Newcomen engine erected in Holland near Rotterdam in 1776. Farey, in his *Treatise on the Steam Engine*, gives an account by an eyewitness of this engine at work,[5] but from drawings that have survived in Holland, it would appear to be not quite accurate.[6] Windmills pumped the water from the land into a storage basin that was the same level as low tide in the river, the tide rising 5 feet higher. The piston in the single steam-cylinder was connected to five parallel beams instead of the usual one. At the end of the beams were five vertical lift pumps, some round and some square, while three smaller pumps were placed half-way between the outside end of the beam and the centre so they had only half the stroke of the other five. These pumps could be disconnected or joined on again individually while the engine was running in order to lessen the load on the engine as the tide rose, or to increase the amount of water pumped as the tide fell. It was a brave attempt to vary the work done by a machine that had a constant power output, but this plan has been found to be defective; for whenever one of the pumps is taken off or disjoined, the engine has too much power for some time; and commonly, when a pump is put on at the ebbing of the tide, she has too little power, and sometimes entirely stands for some time.[7]

A little before this, when he was developing his own engine, James Watt had investigated the possibility of building one in Holland. Writing to Dr Roebuck on 10 February 1769, he said:

Yesterday I received a letter from Mr Enslie, with a particular account of the lake near Rotterdam which, as soon as I have studied a little, I will transmit to you; but, from what I have seen, it will not be a proper place for us, as the greatest part of the expense appears to be surrounding it with a dike, and making a proper outlet into the river. The value of the ground is less, and the number of acres greater, than we were calculating, and the quantity of water raised by the water-mills immense.[8]

But Watt did not give up hope of using his engine for land drainage. In 1782 he received an inquiry from Towers Allen Esq.[9] which he looked upon as "a most desirable opening to a beneficial trade".[10] He was very cautious in his reply, for he considered the "fens to be the only trump card we have left in our hand".[11] Mr Allen used a London address so it has not been possible to discover the area he hoped to drain, and the matter was not pursued any further, but Watt's reply is quoted in full in Appendix I, for it explains the conditions demanded by Boulton and Watt for erecting their steam-engines.

Another inquiry was made in 1789 by the Commissioners of Middle Fen near Ely. They had just obtained an Act of Parliament[12] empowering them to raise more taxes on their lands and to levy tolls on people using their banks. Their area was bounded on the north-east by the River Mildenhall or Lark, to the north and west by the Ouse and Cam, and to the south-east by the hard lands of Isleham, Fordham, Soham and Wicken. One of the Commissioners, Robert Wild, approached Boulton for calculations and costs of a steam-engine which he could lay before a meeting to be held in July. Boulton complied with the request, for Wild and others seemed "to be sure that if one Fen finds benefit that all ye rest will follow ye Example & that 100 Engines will be immediately ordered".[13] But at the meeting, Mr Geo. Stevens, a millwright at Ely, also laid before the Commissioners details supplied by Francis Thompson of an atmospheric engine, with a 40-inch cylinder to raise 60 to 70 hogsheads per minute which would cost £470 if a pump were used or £520 for the same size engine with rotative motion.[14] John Rennie was near by at Bury St Edmunds making a canal survey, and he said that the charges by Boulton and Watt were made in the form of an annual premium, for a rotative engine "£5 or £6·6 per horses power according to situation & for water raising engines 1/3 of the savings of fewil".[15] It will be seen from the letter to Towers Allen in Appendix I that Boulton and Watt did not supply complete engines at this period, which must have deterred many prospective purchasers. In addition Thompson did not demand an annual premium, for where an engine would be used intermittently as in the Fens, a premium on horse-power was considered excessive, although one-third of the savings on fuel was thought more reasonable.[16] Tenders for an engine to raise 160 hogsheads of water were received, £860 from Thompson[17] and £723 without pump from Boulton and Watt,[18] but nothing further was done. Boulton and Watt decided to drop the proposal because they would not enter into competition for any job and they were in doubt "whether we can make any proposal that will prove satisfactory, as your gentlemen seem to wish to have their job done on the cheapest terms without taking into consideration whether that may be the best".[19]

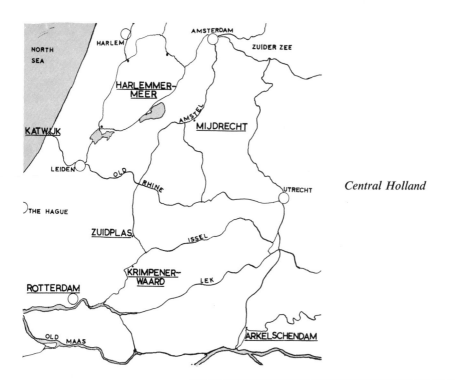

Central Holland

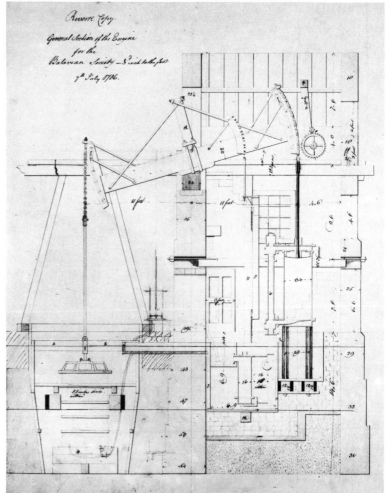

This Boulton and Watt beam-engine, built in 1786 for the Batavian Society, Holland, was the first steam-engine to drain land (B. and W. Coll.)

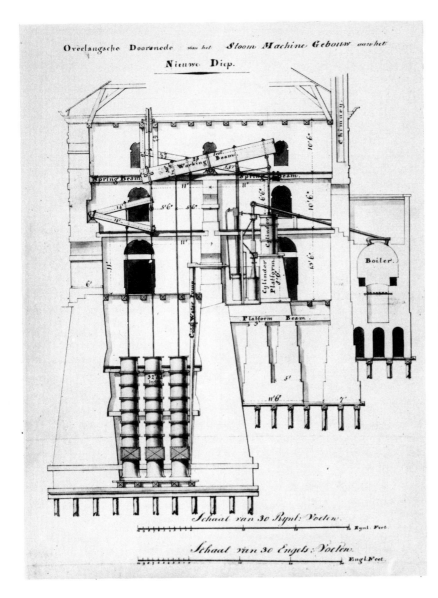

This engine at Nieuwe Diep had three beams and nine pumps (B. and W. Coll.)

In the following year there was an inquiry from Marshland Fen, Norfolk. Jessop made a report and Boulton and Watt were consulted but nothing happened. In the meantime, Watt had built in 1785 a small engine for the Batavian Society to drain the Polder of Blydorp and Kool near Rotterdam. This was only a 22 h.p. engine, and in 1792 a 49 h.p. engine was sent to the Mydrechtsche Polder by the River Amstel near Utrecht. It was not erected until 1794 when it worked 10 strokes per minute against an 18-foot lift.[20] Two more engines followed it, one in 1804 to Krimpenerwaed which raised 575 cubic feet of water per minute from 3 to 7 feet, and a larger one in 1807 on the Katwyk and Rhine Canal which lifted 870 cubic feet $7\frac{1}{2}$ feet in the same time as the former.[21] Although these successfully pumped out the water, they were heavy on fuel and it was thought that steam could not be used economically.

Meanwhile, writers of treatises on agriculture had realized the advantages that would be gained from the introduction of steam-engines for drainage. Among the earliest was the Earl of Dundonald. He gathered that the general bed of the Fens was sufficiently elevated above sea-level to drain itself, and proposed a series of catchwater drains to keep the highland water out of the Fens. He hoped that the Fens would then naturally drain by gravity, but

should the Fens not be capable of being drained completely by any sea level, and that the water should require to be raised, the most judicious method of proceeding would be still to conduct the water to the lowest level, and which will be found to be nearest to the sea, and then by a sufficient number of windmills, or other engines, to lift it over the great sea bank. Some well constructed fire engines would at *certain times* be of material service to the drainage.[22]

Although this may be a good plan in theory, the Earl had not sufficiently studied the Fens, or he would have discovered that some of the lands farther from the sea were lower than the maritime parts.

Most other writers did not consider treating the Fens as a whole, but saw the steam-engine only as a useful supplement to the existing windmills. It sometimes happened that the windmills remained idle through lack of wind for as long as two months and often when there was rain, there would be no wind. Steam-engines could work at any time,[23] even during periods of hard frost because they had enough power to break the ice while windmills remained frozen solid. When this happened, the windmills could not pump until a thaw came, but then the rivers would be in flood and the water-level too high so the windmills still could not work. With a steam-engine, the drains could be cleared during frost when the rivers were low, so when the snow melted the drains would be ready to receive the water.[24]

Most of these early suggestions were for small steam-engines to replace windmills, or even for engines coupled to windmills to work the scoopwheel when there was no wind. To replace a large windmill with an 80-foot sail, a 20 h.p. engine was necessary. This would cost in the region of £1,500, or about the same as a windmill, and burn about twenty bushels of coal during twenty-four hours.[25] These policies prevented the full economies of the steam-engine from being realized. With both windmills and a steam-engine, millers and millwrights still had to be employed, while the steam-engine also required an "engineer" and a stoker, besides which two sets of equipment had to be maintained. A large steam-engine which could do the work of four or five windmills would need only one engineer and one stoker, and there would be an economy in fuel through using a larger machine. During the year there would be long periods when this expensive machinery would be standing idle, so the suggestion was made that the engine could be employed to grind corn when there was no water to pump. Fenland peat would help to reduce the costs, so one writer thought,[26] but obviously he had never tried to fire an engine on it, although during the Second World War, the Maestenbroek engine in Holland was fired with reeds as a desperate measure after the Germans had cut the banks.

In view of the manifest advantages, it may be wondered why the steam-engine was not used earlier in the Fens, but nearly all the districts had some form of investment in drainage works which they were unwilling to scrap without proof of the new methods. For an area which was installing pumping machinery for the first time, it would have been more economical to build one steam-engine instead of many windmills,[27] but in England there were no such areas, and it seemed more reasonable to spend small sums on repairs to existing machinery rather than invest a large sum on something untried. There was also the conservatism of the fenmen to be taken into account, although steam-engines were accepted in England more quickly than in Holland. As late as 1836 it was seriously considered draining the Haarlemmermeer by windmills, and the superiority of the steam-engine was not finally established until after 1850 when the Nootdorp had been drained

Cruquius engine, one of three which drained the Haarlemmermeer in Holland

by a steam-engine in 1844 and the Haarlemmermeer laid dry by three engines in 1852. Even so, these schemes were not carried out with land drainage as the primary object. This was of only secondary importance, and for many years the farmers in the Haarlemmermeer did not prosper. The real reason was to stop these large lakes further eroding their banks and threatening the land with inundation. In 1836 the Haarlemmermeer had extended itself nearly to Amsterdam, so the government was forced to take action, but it was not until 1852 that it was finally laid dry by three steam-engines.

In England there was the same reluctance to try out the steam-engine, but, although none were used at first for land drainage, their use began to become common for other purposes. Arthur Young mentions one of 12 h.p. installed before 1800 by Mr Gooch of Quiddenham to help a water-mill grind corn in times of drought.[28] Many canals, if they had insufficient supplies of water to fill the locks, resorted to steam-engines to keep their summit levels filled. John Rennie suggested that one should be built to supply the Foss Navigation from the Trent so that more water would flow down the Witham to keep that river properly scoured out.[29] Other steam-engines were used on major engineering schemes in the Fens in order to drain the foundations for bridges or sluices or to keep drains dry while they were being dug.

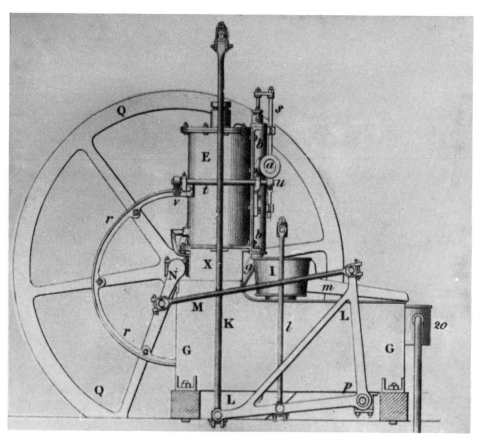

Boulton and Watt double-crank engine which Rennie used to help his work in the East, West and Wildmore Fens; from J. Farey, Treatise on the Steam Engine

When Rennie was engaged in draining the East, West and Wildmore Fens, he employed two steam-engines to pump out water from the works. Boulton and Watt made both engines, the first being set to work during September 1804. This was a 6 h.p. double-crank rotative engine with a 16-inch diameter cylinder and cost £324.[30] It was sent to Tennard and Rodgerson at Boston and had to work so much that there was no time to clean out the boiler. By December the boiler was in such bad condition that another had to be ordered, for Rennie feared that "unless the new one is immediately sent, there is a probability, that the works will soon be stopped by water".[31] The other engine had been delivered to the site by January 1805 but not erected.[32] The Boulton and Watt Engine Book states that an engine for the East, West and Wildmore Fens came from Bough Hollinsworth and Company. Boulton and Watt built two engines for this firm at the beginning of December 1804,[33] the same size, type and cost as the earlier one delivered to Tennard and Rodgerson, but had to resume possession of them because Bough and Hollinsworth ran into financial difficulties.[34] Presumably one of these engines was sold to the Fen Commissioners. These particular engines were removed when the work was finished, for all these Fens were able to have a natural drainage by means of new cuts and outlets to the sea so that no pumping by machinery was necessary.

Various proposals to straighten the outfalls of the main rivers to the sea necessitated steam-engines to keep the new channels dry while the workmen were still digging them. Rennie allowed £10,000 for a "Steam engine for pumping water from the works" in his original survey of 1814 for a new cut for the Nene.[35] In his second report of 1821, he allowed £12,000,[36] but nothing was done in this river until the Nene Outfall Act was passed in 1827. On the River Ouse, his original estimate for £127,639 included the excavation of the cut, a dam at either end of the old course of the river, a bridge over the cut, sundry works at Lynn Harbour, banks and contingencies and £5,500 for a steam-engine.[37] His estimates were attacked, especially by Mr Golborne who allowed only £1,500 for a steam-engine.[38] The final estimates included the improvement of the navigation of various rivers as well as the actual cut. The total was expected to be £149,115 of which £6,050 was for a steam-engine "to take the water during the excavation of the cut".[39] Boulton and Watt supplied a 20 h.p. engine and a pump which with boiler cost in their works £1,189 6s.[40] The steam-cylinder was 36 inches diameter and 7 foot stroke and the pump was 52 inches diameter by 5 feet long.[41] There may have been an accident with this engine, for there was an additional expense of £300 "extra for Damage done by Steam in March last".[42] This engine was removed prior to the opening of the cut.

Mention might be made here of two other engines connected with the Eau Brink, not on land but in boats. One was in a "mud boat" and was used to deepen and scour out the River Ouse between Eau Brink and Denver Sluice.[43] The success of this may have prompted the Bedford Level Commissioners to consider one as well, for they decided to "inquire what would be the charge of hiring or buying a Steam Engine to work a Bear to scour the soft part of the One Hundred Feet River . . . and to use for general purposes".[44] But these plans can not have materialized, for an order was made a year later to try using horses before anything was done about a steamboat.[45] However, during the celebrations that marked the opening of the Eau Brink Cut, several members of the Corporation did venture aboard a steamship.

Several of the Members of the Board present attended a great number of the Eau Brink Commissioners in a Steam Vessel called the Swiftsure immediately before the Meeting in passing up and down the Eau Brink Cut to view the Bridge and works upon the opening, and the other members who attended on shore and the Eau Brink Commissioners being about to dine at the Town Hall at Lynn and having sent an invitation to the Board, Resolved that such of the members as can make it convenient dine with the Commissioners [of the Eau Brink] the expense to the Board [Bedford Level] being paid by the receiver.[46]

The opening of the Eau Brink Cut marks the end of Rennie's association with the Fens owing to his death in the following September, but although most of his schemes were not carried out, he had been concerned with many plans and made many recommendations for the erection of steam-engines to drain the land. A list of the main reports and surveys carried out by him on schemes associated with the Fens is given in Appendix XI. The number of times that he surveyed these districts enabled him to check his figures of heights and distances, and the skill he had gained from work on waterways and canals in other parts of the country enabled him to give the best possible advice. Of all the schemes that he surveyed, only three were carried out in his lifetime. These were the draining of the East, West and Wildmore Fens, the Eau Brink Cut, and the erection of the Swaffham and Bottisham drainage engine, but he influenced the work that was done by others on some projects during his life, while some of his plans were carried out after his death. All of his reports show a thoroughness and a desire to do what was the best course, though not necessarily the cheapest. This must have lost him many contracts, but in the long run it has cost the fenmen dear, for the work would have been carried out more economically in the days of Rennie, and would have saved vast sums since then.

A good example of this is the scheme he proposed for diverting the rivers on the east side of the Fens. Like Vermuyden, he realized that it was necessary to keep the flood water out of the Fens. He proposed digging a channel round the eastern side of the lowlands, using cast-iron aqueducts where necessary. When the rivers had been diverted into this channel, the windmills would work more often and the banks would be safer for there would be no deep floods to hinder the mills or endanger the banks. Rennie even hoped that with this scheme and the Eau Brink Cut, there would be so much additional fall in the rivers to be "sufficient to effect the complete drainage of these Levels without the assistance of Windmills".[47] He estimated that it would cost £1,188,189, but his scheme was never carried out, although a similar one is being implemented today. The Eau Brink Cut that he made was not done as part of this scheme.

The suggestion that Rennie put forward for draining the North Level and South Holland were too expensive for their time, but his proposals had to be carried out within the following twenty years to ensure an adequate drainage. He realized that the crux of the problem lay in the obstructed state of the outfall of the Nene. He therefore proposed a combined scheme to improve the outfall by a new cut below Gunthorpe Sluice, and then to improve the drainage of each area by new internal drains. He estimated that the cost of the works would be £263,604,

but this sum, although large, is very moderate when compared with the immense district of land which will be completely drained by it, amounting to upwards of 80,000 acres, and I apprehend that when the expense of Building, Working and Repairing the windmills now required to keep the land in little better than a half drained state is considered, it will be found that this sum does not very much exceed the present expense of windmill drainage so that the principal part of the benefit which will arise from the improvement of the land will be a clear gain to the Owners and Occupiers.[48]

Later he suggested that two powerful steam-engines should be erected, "to be worked whenever the natural drainage may be obstructed by the River-floods. It is intended to place them near to the Outfalls, and to open a communication between the principal drains for South Holland, the North Level and Wisbech Hundred, so as to admit of the engines working conjointly for the benefit of the three districts."[49] He proposed that the engines should be 50 h.p. each, and to have two rather than one in case any accident occurred to one which would stop it working during the winter.[50] The engines were estimated to cost £10,000 each, and the expenses of working and repairs were expected to be £2,000 each year for the two.[51]

The various parties concerned failed to reach agreement, so two districts were obliged to act independently and erect small steam-engines to drain their own land. For one of these districts, Newborough Fen, Rennie hesitated to recommend a steam-engine for he was

decidedly of opinion that all those kind of measure tend but little towards effecting . . . a complete natural Drainage while the sums of money likely to be expended upon them from time to time is great and will in a few years amount to full as much as the expense of carrying into execution some such scheme as that recommended in my Report to the Bedford Level Commissioners, 26 Jan. 1814.[52]

It was twenty years from the date of his first report before "a perfect natural drainage without the aid of windmills or steam engines and internal banks and works [was] obtained for all the Fens and low grounds lying between the Sea and the North Side of the Nene".[53] Then the North Level internal drains alone cost £150,000[54] when completed in 1834 and a further £200,000 was spent on the Nene Cut and outfall.

Another area which failed to take Rennie's advice was the Waterbeach Level. This land has always been difficult to drain owing to the great depth of peat and its great distance from the sea. The early attempts to drain this part by windmills have already been described, and early inquiries were made about the use of a steam-engine. It would be interesting to know whether the Commissioners of this district had any connexion with the Level of Hatfield Chase, for both areas obtained new Acts of Parliament[55] in the same year, enabling them to erect "Engines" and other works for draining their lands. Hatfield Chase was divided into two sections and the southern part installed a steam-engine in 1813,[56] which was probably the first land-drainage engine in England. Rennie was asked to report on the Waterbeach Level and had no hesitation in recommending a steam-engine. Not only was this Level surrounded on two sides by rivers, the Old West and the Cam, but the highlands of Waterbeach and Denny Hards sent down to the fen a considerable amount of water in times of heavy rain. The level of the land was 3 feet lower than the River Cam so that, since there was little likelihood of the river being lowered owing to the navigational interests, some form of artificial drainage was necessary.

Rennie proposed digging a catchwater drain along the south side of the district to exclude all the highland water by carrying it straight into the rivers. Then "the whole Level of Waterbeach will be so completely surrounded, that no water can get into it except what falls on its own surface".[57] This has never been done so the engines that have since been erected have had to pump out a great deal of highland water. Rennie wished to build the steam-engine at the northern end of the district near the place called Harimeer Corner where the Old West and Cam join, so that it would pump into the Cam at the lowest point. He wrote to Boulton and Watt for an estimate who replied:

We have as you desire, *roughly* calculated the size and cost of an Engine & *Pump* to raise 16,600,600 cubic feet, 8 feet high in Seven Days. A 40 inch 6 ft. str. working 15 to 16 strokes per minute of a 60 inch pump 6 ft. st. would do this; and the metal materials of Engine and pump, including intablature, beam & pillars of iron, would amount to about £2000 or 2000 Guineas.[58]

The building for the steam-engine and a sluice would have cost £3,750 and the total for the complete scheme was £15,000, or over £2 per acre which was considered too great. The Commissioners rejected Rennie's plan and instead built another windmill in 1814 for over £1,000, and in 1831 they installed a steam-engine which cost £5,000, to which must be added work on the drains.

An area where Rennie has not received sufficient credit for the work that was finally done is Deeping Fen. His connexion with this district began in 1800 when, together with Jessop, Maxwell and Hare, he made a report on the state of the drainage and suggested what should be done. The land was drained by the Vernatt's Drain which emptied into the Welland below Spalding. The state of the outfall of that river prevented a proper flow from the Vernatt's Drain, so these engineers suggested that the best solution was to extend the Vernatt's Drain to the Witham where the outlet was better. Since they realized that this would probably cost too much, they recommended that proper engines should be erected at Pode Hole where the drains of Deeping Fen joined the Vernatt's Drain "in order to keep the water, at all times, low enough to enable the private Engines to work into the Common Drains".[59] Seeing that some form of artificial drainage was a necessity,

if Wind Engines are used, they may be made on a much better Construction than any hitherto used in the Fens; but as in calm weather they will frequently be useless, when they be much wanted, we have no hesitation in saying, that the only certain way, without extending Vernatt's Drain as before mentioned, of securing a compleat Drainage, will be to make use of a Steam

Engine. . . . A small one may be sufficient to relieve the Drains, and enable the Private Mills at all times to work, when they have wind; but a large one might be erected, equal to the power of all the present mills.[60]

No steam-engines were erected as recommended by this report and the drainage continued to deteriorate so that further advice was sought from Rennie in 1818. He found the Fen "I may almost say, in a lost state",[61] and again recommended an extension of the Vernatt's Drain to the Witham. But the money could not be raised owing to an agricultural depression, so that he was asked to advise about the possibility of erecting steam-engines. In his reply, he thought that "a Windmill drainage is the most imperfect of all modes and in many cases the adoption of such a mode may be said to be a useless waste of money",[62] and recommended that steam-engines should be built at Pode Hole. He proposed that a counter-drain should be cut beside the banks of Vernatt's Drain to carry back to the engines any water that soaked through the banks from the higher level of water that the engines would maintain in the Drain. This was to prevent the lands adjoining Vernatt's Drain suffering any injury.

Rennie also gave a great deal of attention to the size of engine required, and found it was not easy to calculate because "the rain that falls is not regular throughout the year . . . and the Steam engines ought to have sufficient power to cope with contingencies".[63] He reckoned that 120 h.p. would be necessary, which he proposed to divide into two engines of 60 h.p. each, "as in case of accident to one, the other will be able to perform her work and one set of Duplicate Articles will suffice in place of Two which would be necessary were the engines to be of different sizes".[64] Legal difficulties, and the necessity of obtaining a new Act of Parliament, delayed any start being made on these engines until after Rennie's death. Eventually two engines, one of 60 h.p. and the other of 80 h.p., were built, but they came from different makers so no parts were interchangeable. However, it is obvious that Rennie's advice and plans played a major part in the conception and establishment of this pumping station. His estimate for the total cost was very nearly correct, as was that for the annual running expenses. No doubt had he lived, he would have been asked to supervise the building here as he did at Upware for the Swaffham and Bottisham Level.

By 1820 the first steam drainage engines were at work in the Fens. They had developed into reliable machines, able to produce a type of power that could be easily harnessed for land drainage. The fenmen were beginning to realize the advantages of the steam-engine and, during the following decade, improvements in drainage works and changes in agricultural methods made it a really economic proposition.

NOTES

1. L. T. C. Rolt, *Thomas Newcomen* . . . (1963), p. 36.
2. J. Farey, *A Treatise on the Steam Engine* (1827), p. 117.
3. M. Triewald, *Short Description of the Atmospheric Engine* (1734), p. 47.
4. J. A. Clarke, *Fen Sketches* (1852), p. 246.
5. J. Farey, op. cit., p. 266.
6. I am indebted to Ir. L. Monhemius and Ir. W. Badon Ghijben for this and other information concerning the early Dutch pumping engines.
7. J. Farey, op. cit., p. 266.
8. J. Watt, *Technical Inventions of James Watt* (1854), vol. i, p. 44.
9. B. and W. Coll., Towers Allen to Boulton, 3 December 1782.
10. ibid., Watt to Boulton, 4 December 1782.
11. ibid.
12. 29 Geo. III, c. 22.
13. B. and W. Coll., Boulton to Watt, 6 July 1789.

14. ibid., from R. Wild, 3 September 1789.
15. ibid., from J. Rennie, 2 November 1789.
16. ibid.
17. ibid., from R. Wild, 16 November 1789.
18. ibid., from R. Wild, 28 November 1789.
19. ibid., Watt to R. Wild, 24 November 1789.
20. ibid., Engine Book, p. 288 (Portfolio 564).
21. ibid., Watt to W. Swansborough, 6 August 1814.
22. Earl of Dundonald, *Treatise showing . . . the connection . . . between Agriculture and Chemistry* (1795), p. 193.
23. A. Young. *A. of A.*, vol. 43, p. 569.
24. W. Gooch, *Cambridge* (1806), pp. 239 ff.
25. A. Young, *A. of A.*, vol. 43, p. 569.
26. R. Parkinson, *Huntingdon* (1813), p. 23.
27. W. Gooch, op. cit., p. 239.
28. A. Young, *Norfolk* (1804), p. 73.
29. J. Rennie, Letter Books, vol. 2, p. 439, 26 October 1803.
30. B. and W. Coll., Small Engine Book, 1804–1810, p. 17.
31. ibid., from J. Rennie, 16 December 1804.
32. J. Rennie, Letter Books, vol. 3, p. 232, 1 January 1805.
33. B. and W. Coll., Small Engine Book, 1804–1810, pp. 29 and 33.
34. ibid., from J. Watt to Bough Hollinsworth and Dyson, 28 March 1805.
   Having been put to considerable trouble & inconvenience in preventing our property from being enveloped in the disaster with which you were recently threatened we trust you will see the propriety of our not exposing it again to a similar risk, and we therefore now take the liberty of apprizing you that we have directed our agents not to deliver up possession of the engines until you have pade the amount.
35. J. Rennie, Letter Books, vol. 7, p. 411, 26 January 1814.
36. ibid., vol. 11, 30 January 1821.
37. Committee on the Eau Brink Drainage, 11 March 1818, Mr Harrison, pp. 22 and 26.
38. ibid., p. 26.
39. J. Rennie, Letter Books, vol. 10, p. 420, December 1819.
40. B. and W. Coll., Engine Book, 1816–1823, p. 127.
41. ibid., to J. Rennie, 10 January 1818.
42. J. Rennie, Letter Books, vol. 11, p. 210, 11 July 1820.
43. ibid., p. 109, 3 April 1820.
44. B.L.C., Minute Book, 30 July 1821.
45. ibid., 29 May 1822.
46. ibid., 31 July 1821.
47. J. Rennie, *Report . . . on the Drainage . . . of the South and Middle Levels. . . , 24 May 1809.*
48. J. Rennie, Letter Books, vol. 7, p. 412, 27 January 1814.
49. T. Wing, *Considerations on the Principles of Mr. Rennie's Plans for the Drainage of the North Level . . .* (1820), p. 7.
50. ibid., p. 12.
51. ibid., p. 26.
52. J. Rennie, Letter Books, vol. 10, p. 418, 27 December 1819.
53. ibid., vol. 7, p. 416, 26 January 1814.
54. T. Telford, *Life of Thomas Telford* (1838), pp. 320 and 322.
55. Waterbeach Level, 53 Geo. III, L. & P., c. 81. Hatfield Chase, 53 Geo. III, L. & P., c. 161.
56. J. K. Altes, *Sir Cornelius Vermuyden* (1925), pp. 144 and 201.
57. J. Rennie, Letter Books, vol. 8, p. 23, 5 March 1814.
58. B. and W. Coll., to J. Rennie, 3 March 1814.
59. J. Rennie, Letter Books, vol. 2, p. 199, 11 August 1800. This report was printed and a copy survives in the Lincoln Record Office.
60. ibid., p. 201, 11 August 1800.
61. ibid., vol. 10, p. 5, 16 October 1818.
62. ibid., vol. 11, p. 340, 6 December 1820.
63. ibid., p. 342, 6 December 1820.
64. ibid.

CHAPTER VI

Fine Deep Channels

The years of prosperity during the Napoleonic Wars were followed by two decades of difficulty and slump, especially for the farmers who were faced once more with foreign competition, but great sums of money were invested in all types of projects in the Fens for it was realized that an adequate return on capital could be guaranteed if the drainage could be secured. The most important of these improvements concern the outfalls of the rivers to the sea, thereby not only ensuring a greater certainty for the drainage, but also benefiting the navigation, with the result that agricultural produce could be conveyed away more cheaply and coal could be carried up the rivers for steam pumping engines at less expense. At the same time, roads and bridges were improved, and experiments carried out in agriculture so that at the end of this period, the fenland farmers were still able to make a profit, although the price of wheat and oats had slowly decreased.

The key to this prosperity lay in the cleansing of the outfalls. In spite of their deplorable condition, trade had increased as the Industrial Revolution gathered momentum. The River Ouse was the biggest and most important, and was also the first to be tackled. Through it the water from the whole of the South Level and most of the Middle Level made its way to the sea, and through it was carried the agricultural produce from Cambridgeshire and parts of Bedfordshire, Suffolk and Norfolk. The trade of King's Lynn was very extensive, not only to other parts of England, but also overseas, although in 1818 it was still almost wholly deprived of its foreign trade, and business was nearly confined to the import of coal and the export of corn to other British ports.

Year	Tons of Wine imported	Chaldrons of coals imported	Quarters of corn exported	Amount of revenue
1761	810	64,100	207,700	£ 37,600
1771	1,030	103,900	151,900	58,800
1781	350	69,400	118,800	36,900
1791	1,030	90,600	183,200	56,600
1801	1,280	76,100	195,600	74,800
1806	560	103,700	147,600	84,200
1811	450	115,500	212,500	75,300[1]

The River Ouse was shallow and dangerous above and below the town of Lynn.

It is presumed that the history of tidal rivers does not furnish an instance like that before us, where the upland waters from being confined nearly in a straight line, and to a width of 200 feet (as they are at Germans bridge), are suffered to wander as they approach their outfall into a rambling circuitous course, expanding to a width of nearly a mile, and thence returning to the same line that was before deserted. Internal navigation is rendered so defective, that boats cannot pass from Germans to Lynn without pilots, by means whereof great delays and a vast increase in the expense of freight are occasioned; and in blowing weather many lighters have been sunk, and lives have been lost. Navigation from the port of Lynn to the sea is injured by beds of sand, which are constantly becoming stronger for want of a proper scower, insomuch that no vessels can navigate but such as are of a particular form and structure.[2]

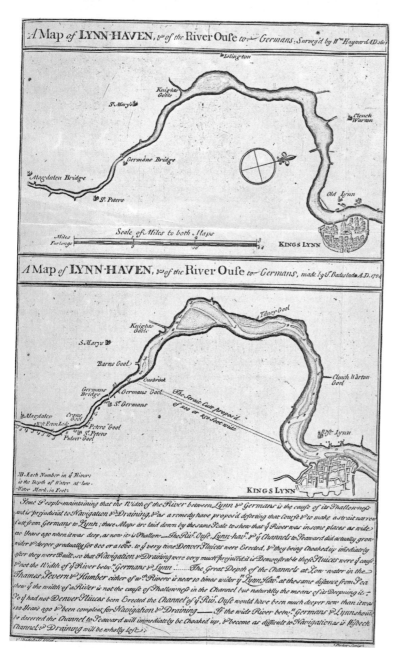

The Eau Brink

The chief obstruction lay between Wiggenhall St Germans and the town of Lynn itself, for here the river turned to the west and completed a semicircle before it bent back again and resumed its former route to the sea. The bed of the river was too broad so that it silted up and the current lost its force and was unable to scour away the sand-banks below the town of Lynn. By straightening out this part, it was hoped that the river would become deeper with the result that

the gangs of lighters may at all times navigate either up or down, with much more expedition and with infinitely less danger than they now do, all the present wide, difficult and uncertain channel from Eau Brink to Lynn. . . . The expenses of bridge pilots saved, the wear and tear of craft, the labour of men, boys and horses lessened; the voyage performed with greater certainty and in much less time than at present.[3]

61

The gangs of boats would no longer have to wait for several days at the different shoals, and the navigation would be continued the whole time without boats unloading their cargoes as they were often obliged to do.[4] The channel below the town would be improved by the greater scouring power that the river would have if it were straightened, and this alone was expected to clear the mouth without resort to artificial aids. Relief was also expected for the drainage concerns, because the water would escape more quickly to the sea. If the danger of floods were lessened, then the banks need not be built so high, and the danger of their breaking would not be so great because the water pressure against them would be less. The normal water-level in the rivers would remain the same through most of the South Level because Denver Sluice maintained the navigation level, but relief was expected for the drainage engines since the floods would subside more quickly. Therefore the Eau Brink scheme was expected to improve both drainage and nagivation.

There was long and bitter argument over the Eau Brink Cut, and the best shape and size were the subject of fierce controversy so that arbitration was necessary. The dimensions to which Rennie and Telford built the Cut as Joint Engineers were stipulated by that decision. By April 1821 the task was nearing completion. To open it, all that was necessary was to remove the banks at either end, and fill in the old course of the river at the top to divert the water down the new channel. Rennie ordered that there should be "a sufficient quantity of clay ready to form the slopes of the said bank, also all the Railway, Sleepers, Plates, Waggons etc to convey the earth and other Materials".[5] The new Cut was formally opened on 31 July 1821,[6] amid many celebrations. Rennie died in the following autumn and his son, later Sir John Rennie, was appointed in his place.[7] He went to Lynn to inspect the works and was very pleased with what he saw, but in fact the Cut had been made too small. Telford was again called in to give advice.

I was solicited by them [the Navigation Commissioners] to act in that capacity [Engineer], to which I agreed, and, in concert with Mr. Rennie [elder], directed the works until the cut was opened in 1821.... Although executed fully to the dimensions fixed by the umpire, the capacity of the Eau-Brink Cut was, upon trial, found to be too small for the river, and was by my advice, enlarged one-third, which was also performed by Messrs. Jolliffe and Banks at an expense of £33,000. [The total cost was a little under £500,000.][8]

The effect of the new cut, after this enlargement, has exceeded expectation. During the first winter after it was opened, the river-channel from Denver Sluice to Lynn was scoured and deepened five feet, on an average; and the mud thus removed being met by the tidal water, at the lower end of the cut at Lynn, was carried up the old river-course, and silted the upper part of it with a twenty-feet sediment in that short space of time; nor did this accretion of soil cease until nearly the whole of the old channel, about six miles in length and a half mile in breadth, was converted into valuable pasture. Between Lynn and Denver Sluice, the whole bed of the river Ouse, including the Eau Brink Cut (which now forms the lower portion of that river) has since gradually deepened itself nearly fifteen feet, on an average, so that the outfall sluices of the drains on each side of the river, and the beds of the drains may now be lowered to a corresponding extent, and the expense and uncertainty of windmills may be in a great measure avoided. Advantage, however, has not been taken of the improved means of drainage afforded by the Eau-Brink Cut in the interior of the Middle and South Levels, so that there are nearly as many windmills as ever, but their efficiency is increased by the more rapid discharge of the waters resulting from the improved outfall.

In regard to the town and harbour of Lynn, the effects of the new cut have been very different from what was expected by the alarmed inhabitants; for the new river, instead of undercutting the wharfs on the town side, has taken a direct course to the sea, and thereby deposited a great body of sand and mud in front of the warehouses and quays, where the vessels formerly lay, which is felt to be a serious inconvenience.[9]

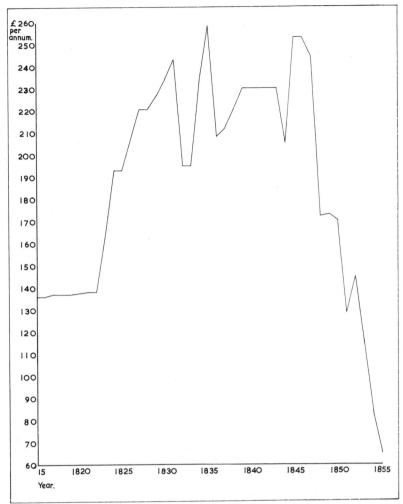

Tolls taken by the Waterbeach Level, 1815–55

Under the Eau Brink scheme, the existing rivers above Denver Sluice were scoured out and their navigation improved, while the Bedford Level Corporation undertook the deepening of the Hundred Foot River. The effect of the Eau Brink Cut on the navigation of the rivers can be studied in the toll receipts of the Waterbeach Level Commissioners. Nearly every local drainage area asked for permission to charge tolls for the use of their banks, and this was originally granted to Waterbeach in 1797 when another Act of Parliament was sought to raise a new tax for paying off debts.[10] The banks that had been built round the Level to keep out the floods were found to form a convenient path for towing barges, but the constant passage of men and horses soon broke them down. Permission was given to levy a toll on every horse or other beast towing boats, with other charges for horses, mares, mules or asses not towing, or droves of cattle, swine, sheep, etc. The money thus raised was to be spent on the upkeep of the banks, so consequently the occupiers of the land and the Bedford Level Corporation were exempt from any tolls. Collecting was farmed out at a public auction, the highest bidder holding the tenure for three years. At first it was difficult to find anyone willing to bid, and the Commissioners themselves had to supervise responsible persons, until in 1801 Mr Robert Giles of the parish of Swaffham offered £83 per

63

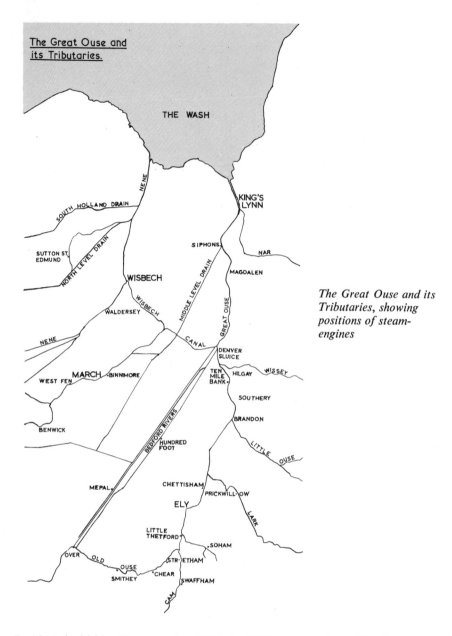

The Great Ouse and its Tributaries, showing positions of steam-engines

annum. In 1811 the bid had increased to £135. In 1813 another Act of Parliament authorized the tolls to be increased[11] and the Account Book shows a receipt of £169 5s. for that year, but in the following year only £135. By May 1821 the amount had risen to £138, but soon there began a steady increase which reached a peak in 1831 of £243 3s.[12] Some boats were still hauled by men so paid no toll, and others found they could avoid payment by crossing over a staunch built at Upware in connexion with the Eau Brink scheme. The accompanying graph of the toll receipts is continued to 1855 to show the effect on waterborne traffic that followed the opening of the railways. After 1855 there was a steady decline throughout the rest of the century until in 1914 the tolls fetched only £9.

How the Eau Brink Cut affected the drainage of the Bedford Level is not so clear. There was direct benefit to those areas, mostly silt land, that lay close to the mouth below Denver Sluice. Here, as Telford says, the Ouse had deepened itself nearly 15 feet, so that most of that area could have natural drainage. Those lands which drained directly into the Hundred Foot River also greatly benefited, for this river is tidal and the average water-level in it would have been considerably lowered. Most of the Middle Level retained a natural drainage until after 1860, although the Sutton and Mepal District installed a steam-engine in 1840, and there were earlier steam-engines near March, but these areas were a long way from the Eau Brink Cut.

Those lands that drained by the Ouse through Denver Sluice still had the same water-level preserved in summer for the navigation. Any land which already lay below river-level, like the Waterbeach and Swaffham districts, would not have been directly affected by the new Cut. Rennie pointed this out to the Commissioners of the Swaffham and Bottisham District when they asked him for advice about the drainage of their land, and accordingly he recommended a steam-engine.[13] This engine and an earlier one built by the Littleport and Downham Commissioners near Denver Sluice remained the only steam-engines in the South Level until 1829 when the second Littleport and Downham engine was built on the bank of the Hundred Foot River. It would seem that the floods were able to pass off more quickly through the Eau Brink Cut, and this enabled the existing windmills to drain the land effectively enough for the standard demanded at that time. Complaints about the drainage in the Waterbeach Level Minute Book die out until the age-old problem of the Fens began to assert itself again. With better drainage, the peat shrank and disappeared so that the level of the land fell. Then drainage slowly worsened and the effects of this were being felt by 1830. This time there was no Eau Brink scheme on which hope for an improvement could be placed. While there was the possibility of such a scheme, it was not worth while for a small area to embark on the costly experiment of steam drainage. But by 1830, there was only the choice of each individual district improving its own drainage by means of steam-engines, or the whole of the South Level embarking on some costly scheme of cut-off rivers such as that suggested by the elder John Rennie. Therefore the Eau Brink Cut, while perhaps delaying the general introduction of the steam-engine to the South Level for a few years, in the end convinced people that there was no other alternative for an adequate drainage except at very great expense.

The success of the Eau Brink Cut no doubt encouraged those who were already trying to start a similar plan for the River Nene. Like the Eau Brink, plans for improving the rest of the channel below Kinderley's Cut can be traced back for many years, but fresh impetus seems to have been given by the erection of the steam-engine for Borough Fen. Borough Fen is the lowest part of the North Level, and had been exempted from paying North Level drainage taxes by an Act of Parliament.[14] Fresh Acts were obtained in 1812 and 1819[15] for the improvement of the drainage, which resulted in the enclosure of the land and an attempt to form a township complete with parish church in the middle of the newly drained area. In 1819 it was proposed to install a steam-engine in order to guarantee regular drainage, but it was feared that the water from the engine would not only seep through the banks of the other North Level lands, but would keep the water in the main drain at such a height that the existing windmills would be unable to work. Therefore Tycho Wing, Agent for the Duke of Bedford who owned large parts of the rest of the North Level, tried to persuade the Borough Fen Commissioners not to erect their engine, but to combine with the other districts in a comprehensive drainage scheme for the whole area. Wing realized that the real problem for the North Level drainage was the choked outfall of the Nene, which prevented the water running out of the North Level drains at Tydd Gote, so he began actively campaigning for the Nene Outfall Cut to help relieve the drainage of the North Level as well as benefit the neighbouring areas. About the existing state of the navigation of the Nene he wrote:

Welney Suspension Bridge, opened 16 August 1826

Pilots are required for the whole distance between Wisbech and the Eye; the expense from the town to Kinderley's Cut is 7/6 and from thence to the Eye the charge is proportional to the draught of the ship at the rate of 2/– per foot. Gangs of lighters are sometimes sunk in winter, and, when the channel is bad, the barges are obliged to meet the large vessels at the Eye; on these occasions an extra freight is charged of 12/6 for each barge: and when a ship is detained upon the sands, losses are likely to occur by the neglect and plunder of the bargemen. At present merchants are afraid of sending ships to Wisbech in consequence of the expense.

As to the navigation between Wisbech and Peterborough, gangs of lighters are the only vessels employed upon that part of the river and in the summer these are frequently detained five or six or sometimes 10 or 12 days at a spot called Northy Grave about three miles below Peterborough.[16]

Partly at Wing's instigation a Committee met and made a report in August 1821, in which they resolved as the first and most important operation to undertake to make a new cut from Crabb Hole to Gunthorpe Sluice, "this new cut being the foundation of all the other improvements, and combining in itself the most important benefits to drainage and navigation".[17] The money was to be raised by a tax laid on the lands draining by the improved outfall and on the navigation which would be benefited by the proposed operations.[18] But the Committee came to the conclusion that, "from the depressed state of the landed interests, and the peculiar circumstances of the country, it was inexpedient to prosecute the scheme at the present time".[19]

In addition to the river interests, there was a plan to build a new road across the mud-flats from King's Lynn to Holbeach and Spalding. When the financial position had improved, both these projects were started in conjunction with each other. The main feature of the road was the building of Cross Keys Bridge, now called Sutton Bridge, which was built on dry land where the course of the Nene was to run when the outfall cut was finished. This helped to reduce the expense, although the road and bridge were estimated to cost £130,000.[20] Mention might here be made of another bridge built at this time, the suspension bridge over the Hundred Foot River at Welney. This was opened on

16 August 1826.[21] There was also a new bridge over the Eau Brink, and in 1830 the Dean and Chapter of Ely Cathedral, who had been responsible for maintaining the ferry across the river to Soham, invited public subscriptions for a bridge.[22]

The Nene Outfall Cut was to begin near Gunthorpe Sluice and run for four and three-quarter miles to Skate's Corner, from where it would reach a further mile to low water at Crabb Hole.[23] The contract was signed by Messrs Jolliffe and Banks on 2 July 1827, and within a short time, over a thousand men were employed so that the work progressed quickly.

On the 4th. of June, 1830, the dam at the lower end being removed, and the upper dam on the 7th., the tide was admitted to flow up the new cut, and this continued until the 14th., but while the river was permitted to pass partly down the old channel, there was not a sufficient rush of water down the new cut to scour out the silt brought by the flowing tide; so that it became absolutely necessary to close the old channel by making an embankment across it, so as to turn the whole of the river down the new cut.[24]

The bed of the new Cut had been purposefully not dug to its proper depth, for it was realized that the tides and river would soon scour it out, and money could be saved, but the whole work was nearly lost through leaving both channels open. Three hundred workmen with one hundred carts were employed day and night to close up the old river, and performed this in six days, with the help of four or five barges or lighters which were sunk across the river course to accelerate the formation of a bank. Once the river was confined

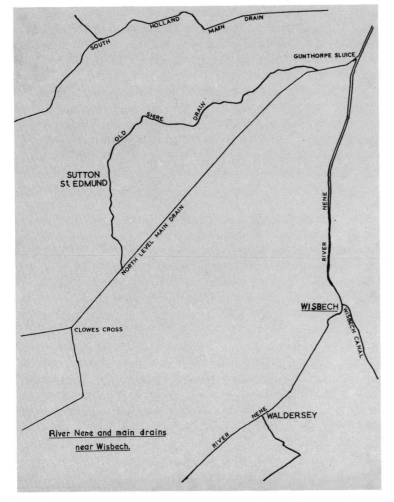

River Nene and Main Drains near Wisbech

to the new channel, all went well, and the water soon scoured out the bottom until there was deep water all the way up to Wisbech. Telford again describes the improvements which resulted.

There is now a safe and daily communication between Wisbech and the sea at all periods of the tides, and in all weather, for vessels of the above [60 tons] burden, and on spring tides for ships of much larger capacity, and drawing not less than fourteen feet of water. Vessels carrying 400 tons reach Sutton Wash on spring tides. . . . The trade of the port, which before the Nene Outfall was made was not more than 50,000 tons a year, has since progressively increased, and reached in the last year to 108,000 tons [1836].[25]

The improvement in the drainage for most areas was equally great. For those parts below Wisbech, the extra fall gained in the river was enough to give all the silt lands a natural drainage without using engines of any sort. Although two steam-engines, one in Borough Fen and one in Sutton St Edmund, had been built before the end of 1820, no more were built in this area until after the Nene Outfall Cut had been completed. Obviously, it was felt unwise to build a steam-engine in any one area when a subscription would have to be paid towards a new Cut which would give a natural drainage. After the internal drainwork had been improved, both of the existing steam-engines were found to be redundant and were removed. These were on the sea side of Wisbech, but nothing was done in that town to straighten the river or widen the bridge. The narrow course of the river impeded the floods, so that those districts which lay beyond Wisbech benefited little from the Nene Outfall Cut. When this was realized, the Waldersea Level was the first to install a steam-pump in 1832, and other areas followed later.

The outfall of the Welland was very defective and the navigation there much impeded. Large tracts of fens and low grounds, including Deeping Fen and the land lying between Spalding and Wyberton, were liable to be overflowed and drowned by the rain and floods.[26] An Act was passed in 1794, but the work was only partially carried out. Although the river was improved for a distance of three miles, the remainder of the Cut was not finished. In 1824 an amended Act was passed but nothing was done and the outfall continued to deteriorate until a further Act was obtained in 1837 when some work was started.[27] The Witham was in much the same condition. The Grand Sluice, built at Boston in 1761, was so frequently silted up that boats to Horncastle or Sleaford went by way of the Trent and the Fossdyke rather than by Boston.[28] Some work was done on the river before 1830, but the outfall still remained bad, and it was another thirty years before that problem was really solved.

By means of these new cuts, the produce of the Fens could be transported more easily, cheaply and quickly to other parts of Britain. Special boats were built to take sheep to the expanding towns of the Midlands, and ships could take grain anywhere by sea.[29] All this gave a stimulus and incentive to improve the agriculture in the Fens, for there were few areas with equal transport facilities. Not only were the main rivers navigable and connected to the canal system of the rest of England, but boats could go up many of the main drains, so that nearly every farm had direct access to some form of water transport. Some of the lodes and drains were quite small, so the goods had to be transhipped into bigger boats.[30] In the East, West and Wildmore Fens, Rennie especially designed the drains large and deep enough for boats, and in addition had three storehouses built where goods could be "protected until they are conveyed to their respective places".[31] When the North Level Main Drain was cut in 1832, it was made navigable as far as Clough's Cross where the loading bays still remain, although the water is kept too low for navigation now. In their day, these inland navigations were of great value to "individuals, and to society at large – they give aid to agriculture, and spirit to trade; and tend to lessen the number of horses which are the greatest devourers of the produce of the earth".[32] On some rivers there were regular passenger-boats, like the one from Cambridge to Ely which did the journey in six hours,[33] and the one along the Nene from Wisbech to Peterborough "which proves very convenient to travellers, in their progress, to or from the great north road".[34] Steamboats were quickly introduced and the rivers were constantly full of traffic.

The waterways in the Fens were mainly used for drainage with navigation as only a secondary consideration. The only canal intended first as an improvement to the nagivation with only minor drainage works was never a financial success. This was the Wisbech Canal which began in the Nene at Wisbech, passed through Outwell, and finished in the River Ouse at Salter's Lode Sluice. It was opened in 1797,[35] and was of great service in draining the neighbourhood, and did benefit Wisbech and the adjacent country considerably by the increase of trade.[36] It really failed because it did not have sufficient supplies of water. In the summer, the only way of maintaining the water-level was to let water in from the Nene at spring tides, so that boats often had to wait until such a high tide before they could use the canal. Salt water, let in to keep up the level, soaked into the adjoining land and the farmers demanded compensation. The scheme was received with considerable enthusiasm when it was first proposed, and the Inaugural Meeting was crowded, but owing to the troubles with which it was beset, the shareholders gained very little on their investment, and the drainage interests benefited at their expense.

The vital importance that people in those days gave to water communications is shown by the persistence of schemes for the London to Cambridge Canal. The potential trade seemed highly encouraging, and various prospectuses showed what might have been carried. Rennie wished to have a line that would go as near as possible to Reach and Burwell, where there were immense supplies of excellent lime and building stone which could not be developed because the expense of land carriage was too heavy.[37] His report was followed by a plan that

was offered to parliament about five years since, (but was rejected) to make a canal from the Brandon River to London. . . . The ports of Lynn and London would have been united. . . . The exuberant produce of the country would have a cheap and expeditious transfer to the metropolis, where these supplies are so essential to the support of its inhabitants, that without them they cannot exist. It appears by Mr. Kent's report, that the export of corn, grain, and flour, from Norfolk, is about 600,000 quarters annually, the greatest part goes to the London market. . . . The estimate in the saving in the price of land carriage alone, is not exaggerated if taken at £200,000 a year. . . . To demonstrate this, it will be enough to state that the price of land carriage from Thetford (situated on the Brandon River) to London, or back, is £4 a ton; and by the proposed canal, the calculation was under 20s.[38]

But wiser policies prevailed, for it was beginning to be realized that "without coalmines or a great demand for coals, lime etc., and the establishment of immense manufactures, canals are too precarious a speculation, for the ready advancement of great subscriptions".[39] Although Parliamentary sanction was obtained in 1813, only a few earthworks near Bishop's Stortford were begun and never completed.

While corn was the main export from the Fens, the main import was coal. Before 1830, there was a tax on seaborne coal, which was sold by chaldron, but no tax on coal carried by land or inland waterway, which was often sold by the ton. The Cornish tin-miners had found this tax ruinous when they began to use steam-engines to drain their mines, and in 1730 the mine captains petitioned the government to remit the duty. The tax made pumping by steam uneconomic until, in 1741, when their pleas were at last heeded, it is said there

Gang at work, "banking"   (*C.O.C.*)

was only one steam-engine at work in the Duchy.[40] The Earl of Dundonald suggested that fire-engines employed in such a great and national object as draining the Fens might be exempted from the duty, for he thought that the benefit which would accrue through the improvement in agriculture would far outweigh the revenue received from the tax. He also pointed out the anomaly of taxing coal carried by one particular way of transport and thought it "truly astonishing that so glaring an absurdity has not hitherto been corrected".[41] Of course, the tax had originally been imposed before the extensive network of canals had been envisaged, and this led to the situation where those areas that could easily be supplied by canal obtained their fuel at a much lower price than the places that could only be supplied by sea. At the turn of the century, the cost of coal at the pithead might be as little as 2*s.* 6*d.* a ton, while at Bury St Edmunds it cost 26*s.* and in London from 43*s.* to 50*s.* a ton.[42]

In addition to the tax on sea coal, the coal brought into the Fens had also to face substantial charges for transport through the difficult outfalls of the river. Some of these charges are given by Wing for the River Nene.

The Newcastle Coal ships, which carry from eighty to an hundred tons, unload into the smaller barges at Sutton Wash-way: the expense of unloading and the barge freight to Wisbech amount to four shillings and six pence per chaldron (Freight 3/–, Porterage etc 1/6) or rather more than three shillings and six pence per ton. . . . The tides must be generally half-sprung before ships coming in can reach Sutton Wash-way; and with vessels going out great alacrity is necessary to dispatch them at the height of the tides; it sometimes happens that being too late they are left during the neaps upon the sands, and are obliged to wait for eight or ten days till the next spring-tides are high enough to carry them off: under such circumstances considerable damage is frequently sustained both by the ship and cargo.[43]

To these charges there had to be added the expense of pilots and the extra price charged by merchants to cover the risks involved. The revenue derived from coal was too important to be surrendered, and the increase of government expenditure during the Napoleonic Wars "led to another increase [in the sea coal tax] of 5 per cent in 1797, and yet another in 1803; while a final war impost of $12\frac{1}{2}\%$ in 1809 brought the import duties to their highest point of 12/6 a chaldron. The last addition was dropped in 1815; and in 1824 the duties were lessened by three-quarters; and all these duties were abolished in 1831"[44] to operate from the beginning of 1832.[45] The effect of the tax was to raise the price of coal by about twenty-five per cent. After 1832 the number of steam-engines employed in the Fens increased very rapidly, no doubt helped by the repeal of the tax on seaborne coal which lowered the annual running expenses.

One further important effect that followed the improvement of the outfalls was the rebuilding of many river-banks. The banks had increased in size as the level of the land had gradually sunk through drainage operations, but at first no scientific thought was given to their construction. Soil was dug from the land side of the bank and thrown on top to make it higher, but this practice undermined the foundations, and sometimes in a flood it collapsed into the hole from where the soil had been taken. Also the banks were often badly situated with regard to the lie of the river. Arthur Young went to inspect the Waterbeach Level just before it was enclosed, and walking down the Cam from Clayhithe he found the banks in a very bad state, "in general for want of the usual and obvious precaution of leaving a foreland between the bank and the river, which washes the foundation, and wears it incessantly, by which means whatever breaches happen are in these places. At present the floods in winter damage these fens greatly, being sometimes a foot under water."[46] These banks were so bad that Young doubted whether it would be worth while enclosing this district.

The soil that was usually used to make the banks was any which was most convenient to obtain, in other words, peat. The result was that the water always soaked through all the fen-banks, and a great part of the water that had been pumped out during the day soaked back during the night upon the same land again.[47] This water destroyed the winter wheat and all the best natural and artificial grasses and prevented the land from being sown until very late in the season.[48] Those who were advocating the proposed outfall cuts pointed out that among the other advantages this soak through the banks would be lessened because the water-level would be lowered.

The consequence will be a saving in the *expense* of internal drainage, because the head of water being lowered against the banks, the soak through them will be decreased, and the banks will not be required to be supported to so great a height as they now are, and the size and consequent expense of engines, will be lessened in the same proportion as the banks and the soak through them are decreased. It will be given in evidence that the saving in internal drainage will be at least one shilling *per* acre for ever on all lands draining by engines.[49]

Although most farmers would not have consented to lower their banks, it was possible to stop leakage by "puddling". The plan of this improved banking was to dig along the bank parallel to the river a trench or

gutter eighteen inches wide, through the old bank down to the clay, (the fen substratum being generally clay). The gutter is afterwards filled up in a very solid manner with tempered clay, and to make the clay resist water, a man in boots always treads the clay as the gutter is filled up. As the fen moor lies on a clay, the whole expense of this cheap, improved and durable mode of water-proof banking, costs in the fens only sixpence per yard.[50]

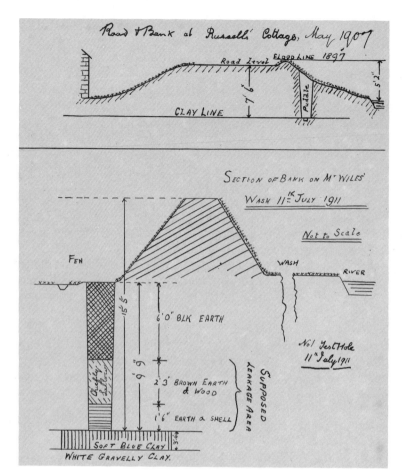

Road & Bank at Russell's Cottage, May 1907

FLOOD LINE 1897

Road Level

CLAY LINE

Puddle

SECTION OF BANK ON Mr WILES'
WASH 11th JULY 1911

Not to Scale

FEN

WASH

RIVER

6'0" BLK EARTH

2'3" BROWN EARTH & WOOD

1'6" EARTH & SHELL

SUPPOSED LEAKAGE AREA

No 1 Test Hole
11" July 1911

SOFT BLUE CLAY

WHITE GRAVELLY CLAY.

Sections through the Water-beach Level banks

The same method was recommended by Rennie to Lord William Bentinck for a sea-bank near Lynn, no doubt through experience he had gained from canal practice.[51] It was sometimes difficult to find suitable clay, and many legal obstacles prevented the adoption of these new waterproof banks,[52] but there was a gradual improvement so that soakage was slowly lessened. When the banks had been puddled, the engines had to pump out only that water which fell upon the surface of the fen or that which ran into the fen from the higher ground, so there was a saving in cost and a greater certainty in drainage.

All of these improvements stimulated economic activity throughout the Fens. The improvement in navigation lowered the cost of transport, so the fenland agricultural products were better able to compete in distant markets. The cost of importing coal was reduced, and this coupled with the abolition of the sea coal tax helped to make steam drainage an economic proposition. Puddling the banks reduced the volume of water that had to be pumped from the land, and the new outfall cuts cleared away the floods more quickly so there was less danger of the banks breaking and the engines could work more efficiently. In these ways the whole aspect of fen drainage was changed during the 1820s, and the steam-engine at last became a practical proposition. One more important change took place in this period, but that will be described under the effects on agriculture, so now the actual introduction and building of steam-engines will be studied.

NOTES

1. W. Richards, *The History of Lynn* (1812), p. 162.
   A similar increase can be seen in the River Nene at Wisbech, for which town W. Watson, *An Historical Account of . . . Wisbech* (1827), p. 312, gives the following figures:
   1805, 29,242 tons handled.
   1810, 23,639   ,,   ,,
   1815, 38,995   ,,   ,,
   1820, 62,030   ,,   ,,
   1825, 70,321   ,,   ,,
   The corn sent coastwise in the year 1826 was about 121,000 quarters, with about 37,680 chaldrons of coals imported and about 7,470 tons of other merchandise.
2. W. Gooch, *Cambridge* (1811), p. 211.
3. ibid., p. 214, extract from James Golborne.
4. ibid., p. 216.
5. John Rennie, Letter Books, vol. 12, p. 79, 30 April 1821.
6. B.L.C., Minute Book, 31 July 1821, see p. 55.
7. Sir John Rennie, *Autobiography* . . . (written 1867 but published unrevised in 1875), p. 160.
8. S. Wells, *The History of the Drainage of . . . Bedford Level* (1830), vol. I, p. 767.
   Sometime after its opening, the dimensions were found to be too contracted, and, in the year 1826, the area of the channel was widened, under a contract with Sir Edward Banks, for the sum of £33,000. . . . Probably the total cost of the Cut, and of all the works connected therewith, will amount to little less than the enormous sum of £500,000.
9. T. Telford, *Life of Thomas Telford* . . . (1838), p. 105.
10. 37 Geo. III, c. 88.
11. 53 Geo. III, c. 81. The tolls which could be levied were:
    1797   1813
    1/-   1/4   for every Horse or other beast towing boats from Harrymere Head to the Brewhouse, Waterbeach, and from Harrymere Head to Stretham Ferry.
    3d   4d   ,, ,, Ass towing a boat.
    1d   ½d   ,, ,, Horse, mare, mule, or Ass not towing a boat.
    10d   1/3   per score for every drove of oxen or other neat cattle and so in proportion, if under 5, 1 penny per head. [1797, ½d.]
    5d   10d   ,, ,, for every Drove of swine, calves, sheep or lambs.
12. The figures for tolls prior to 1813 are taken from the Waterbeach Level Order Book, and after 1813 from the Account Book.
13. J. Rennie, Letter Books, vol. 11, p. 28, 2 February 1820, and subsequent correspondence.
14. 27 Geo. III, c. 2.
15. 52 Geo. III, c. 143, and 59 Geo. III, c. 77.
16. Thorney Letter Books, 7 February 1820.
17. Report on the Outfall of the River Nene, August 1821, p. 4.
18. ibid., pp. 5 and 11.
    It was also resolved
    to convert the present course of the river in the town of Wisbech into a floating harbour, by erecting a dock gate at a point below and another at a point above the town. . . . Vessels would be able to approach and take in and deliver their ladings at the granaries and wharfs as they now do and would be protected from floating bodies of ice.
    Some of the taxes they proposed to levy were:
    1) An annual tax of two shillings and six pence per acre upon the North Level, containing forty eight thousand acres; and upon Wisbech Hundred containing twenty-five thousand, seven hundred acres, which will produce a yearly income of £9,212. 10. 0. in as much as those districts will be freed by the intended improvements from all risk of innundation, and will obtain a very improved drainage by natural means, without the expense of working and maintaining their present mills.
    2) A yearly tax of two shillings per acre on four thousand acres in Sutton St. Edmunds' as they will obtain an improved drainage without the expense of maintaining any engines £400. . . .
    5) A duty of two shillings per chaldron upon coals, and of two shillings and six pence per ton upon all goods navigating between Crabb Hole and Wisbech, calculated at thirty thousand chaldrons of coals, and twenty thousand tons of other goods annually: in consideration of the great saving of expense, and the increased safety and expedition which will result to the navigation from the intended improvements. £5,500. . . .
    10) An additional duty of one shilling and six pence per ton on the navigation from Wisbech to Peterborough, estimated at twelve thousand tons per annum. £900.
19. ibid., p. 13.
20. J. Priestley, *An Historical Account of the Navigable Rivers* . . . (1831), p. 500.

21. W. Watson, *Historical Account . . . of Wisbech* (1827), p. 552.
   The bridge is one hundred and ninety feet long, and in breadth fourteen feet; the platform or road of the bridge springs two feet in the centre and five feet six inches above the general level of the bank, with a neat iron railing, five feet high, and a three feet walk on each side for foot passengers. The bridge is supported by four principle suspending chains, driven twelve feet into the ground, rivetted end to end, and properly secured by coupling plates and bolts of proportional strength, with perpendicular suspenders supporting the lower bars, on which the beams of the bridge rest; the suspension rods are of different length, being nineteen in number on each side. The foundation of the structure consists of sixteen strong piles of timber to each of the two piers, driven twenty one feet in the solid bed of gravel. A large iron plate, fixed twelve feet in the ground, forms a sort of bed, called the anchor, through which the chains run, and to which they are fastened. The piers of the brickwork are twelve feet high, and the cast iron piers twenty-one feet, making in all thirty-three feet from the foundation to the top of the pier.
22. Waterbeach Level Order Book, May 1830.
23. J. Rennie, *Reports as to the Wisbech Outfall. . .* , 26 January 1814.
24. T. Telford, op. cit., p. 113.
25. ibid., p. 320.
26. J. Priestley, op. cit., p. 709, also 34 Geo. III, c. 102.
27. W. H. Wheeler, *The History of the Fens of South Lincolnshire* (2nd ed. 1897), pp. 298 ff.
28. J. Rennie, Letter Books, vol. 3, 28 April 1807.
   The trade of Lincoln is now perhaps greater from the Westward than from the Eastward.
   J. Priestley, op. cit., p. 365.
29. A. Young, *Lincoln* (1799), p. 405.
30. J. Rennie, Letter Books, vol. 6, p. 401, 26 November 1811.
31. ibid., vol. 3, p. 234, 1 January 1805.
32. N. Kent, *Norfolk* (1794), p. 18.
33. E. Carter, *History of the County of Cambridge* (1753).
34. W. Richards, op. cit., p. 111.
35. J. Priestley, op. cit., p. 720.
36. W. Watson, op. cit., p. 312; W. Gooch, op. cit., p. 291.
   30 Oct 1792. The meeting was fully attended, not only by the inhabitants of Wisbech, but by numbers from the midland counties, who showed great anxiety to obtain shares. . . .
      However convenient the communication and intercourse have been found, very little benefit has yet resulted to the shareholders and proprietors.
37. J. Rennie, Letter Books, vol. 1, p. 86, 16 February 1789.
38. N. Kent, op. cit., p. 190.
39. A. Young, *Norfolk* (1804), p. 490.
40. L. T. C. Rolt, *Thomas Newcomen . . .* (1963), p. 121.
41. Earl of Dundonald, *Treatise showing . . . connection . . . between Agriculture and Chemistry* (1795), p. 193.
42. T. S. Ashton and J. Sykes, *Coal Industry of the Eighteenth Century* (1929), p. 236.
   Direct comparison is invalidated by reason of the higher quality of sea-borne coal as well as by slight variations in local weights and measures. . . . Nevertheless it can hardly be doubted that inland coals were generally cheaper than those brought by sea, and the difference must have been of some moment in determining the localisation of industry before the removal of import duties in 1831.
43. T. Wing, *Considerations on the Principles of Mr. Rennie's Plans for the Drainage of the North Level . . .* (1820), p. 16.
44. T. S. Ashton and J. Sykes, op. cit., p. 248.
45. 1 & 2 Wil. IV, c. 6.
46. A. Young, *A. of A.*, vol. 43, p. 45 (1805).
47. R. Parkinson, *Huntingdon* (1813), p. 21.
48. W. Gooch, op. cit., p. 246.
49. G. Maxwell, *Huntingdon* (1793), p. 42.
50. W. Gooch, op. cit., p. 247.
51. J. Rennie, Letter Books, vol. 6, p. 28, 19 June 1809.
52. R. Parkinson, op. cit., p. 21.

CHAPTER VII

Trusty Steam the Office Fills

The decision to erect a steam-engine rested with the commissioners of each local drainage authority. Consequently, there was no general policy throughout the Fens, but each district proceeded as it thought best. There was considerable prejudice in some areas against the steam-engine, while in other places there were legal difficulties to be surmounted. Each body of commissioners had its own problems or conditions to which the steam-engine had to be adapted, so the story of how these engines were built differs in every case. For some areas, many of the original documents have survived to tell the story, and three engines still remain in the Fens. But others have vanished almost without trace or memory.

SUTTON ST EDMUND

The engine that was probably the first to be used in the Fens solely for land drainage falls into the category of forgotten engines. The records and minutes of meetings of the Commissioners responsible for this area cannot be traced, so it has not been possible to discover the exact history of this engine. At the time when it was installed, there had been no improvements to the mouth of the Nene, and the North Level still drained along the twisty route of the old Shire Drain past Sutton St Edmund, through Tydd St Giles, and into the Nene at Tydd Gote. A series of levels taken by Anthony Bower shows why there was a greater need for better drainage of the Sutton St Edmund Fen than elsewhere in that neighbourhood. He compared the heights of land in various places with the cill of Hobhole Sluice. "The height of the land by Sutton St. Edmund's Mill is 11 ft. 6 in. above Hobhole Sluice cill, in Thorney North Fen, 13 ft., in Peterborough Low Fen, 12 ft. 6 in., in Peterborough Great Fen, 13 ft. 2 in."[1] Sutton St Edmund's mill was built on an old rodden and would have been higher than the surrounding lands, so that Fen may have been the lowest in this particular district. It is interesting that this area should also have needed a windmill to drain it in 1664 when windmills were not very common in the Fens.[2]

The first definite mention of this engine is in August 1820 by Tycho Wing, who was Agent for the lands owned by the Duke of Bedford in the North Level. He was examining the expenses that would be saved when the Nene Outfall Cut had been completed.

The expenses of the Engines now used and which would be no longer necessary.

		Acres	Engines
The North Level and Porsand containing		48,000 have	43
Wisbech North Side, Tyd and Newton —		17,700 —	12
Waldersea and Begdale	—	8,000 —	4
Sutton St. Edmund's	—	5,700 —	2
		79,400	61

Of these forty three are large and seventeen small windmills; the charge of working and maintaining the former is eighty pounds, the latter twenty five pounds per annum on an average from the last ten years: Sutton Saint Edmonds has one Steam Engine, the yearly expense of working and repairing which is laid at two hundred pounds per annum.[3]

75

He also states in a footnote that this engine "has only a twelve horse power . . . and drains upwards of 4,000 acres".[4] That he is able to give a definite yearly expense for working the engine shows that it had been running for perhaps two or three years by this time.

From the foregoing, it seems reasonable to assume that this is the steam-engine which a Committee of the Littleport and Downham District went to view "near Wisbech"[5] between 12 and 21 May 1818. On the latter date, this Committee "reported that from every Enquiry and Observation they could make on view of the same, they are of the opinion that a Steam Engine would be most beneficial to the drainage of this [Littleport] District".[6] But the steam-engine was not existing in late 1813 when John Rennie wrote his *Reports as to the Wisbech Outfall and the Drainage of the North Level and South Holland* (dated 26 January 1814). The map accompanying this report shows two windmills draining the area of Sutton St Edmund. It is possible that an inquiry about a steam-engine made in August 1814 by William Swansborough to Boulton and Watt was for this area, for Watt replied that

The engine . . . capable of raising 500 cubic feet of water . . . would be about the equivalent to the power of 10 horses, though we do not make use of that comparison when speaking of engines as applied to raising water as a statement of the actual effect to be produced furnishes a more exact criterion of the power.[7]

It is possible that the engine was erected soon after 1816 when a Bill was granted by Parliament "For the better draining of South Holland".[8] Sutton St Edmund was not included in this area, so there was no improvement in the drainage and the farmers were forced to do something themselves.

The lack of reference to this engine in other writers is due to its geographical position. The Bedford Level does not extend as far as this, so Wells has no need to mention it.[9] It lies just inside the Lincolnshire border, but does not come into the South Holland drainage area. The writers about Cambridgeshire have no cause to include it, whilst the early writers about Lincolnshire do not appear to have penetrated into these remoter recesses of the Fens. However, R. G. Baker, in his Map of Cambridgeshire,[10] does go outside his boundaries and shows a square house with "Steam Engine" beside it about half a mile south of Guanock House. This engine is also marked on the Ordnance Survey Map of 1825 and Wells's Map of the Bedford Level, published by the Fen Office in March 1829, which shows the steam-engine on the south side of the Drain and a windmill on the north. Wheeler states that this "mill, after being superseded by a steam engine, was pulled down in 1838",[11] so the windmill was retained to assist the steam-engine. The steam-engine may have been taken out of service before the windmill, for the drainage was greatly improved when the Nene Outfall Cut was opened in June 1830, and any form of artificial drainage was certainly made redundant when the North Level Main Drain was finished in 1834.[12] The engine was probably removed soon afterwards, and, since building material was expensive in those days, the engine-house was pulled down and the bricks used elsewhere. An investigation of the site has shown the stunted growth of crops in the vicinity, and many remains of broken bricks and stones, which prove that a building did exist here on top of the firmer foundation of a rodden. Now the Shire Drain is only a very minor waterway, and nothing else remains to mark the place where the windmill and steam-engine once pumped.

TEN-MILE BANK

The following gentlemen, Mr Page, Mr Jos. Little, Mr Chas. Martin, Mr Airs, Mr Luddington, Mr Folles, Mr Booton, Mr Hopkins and Mr Smith, all Commissioners of

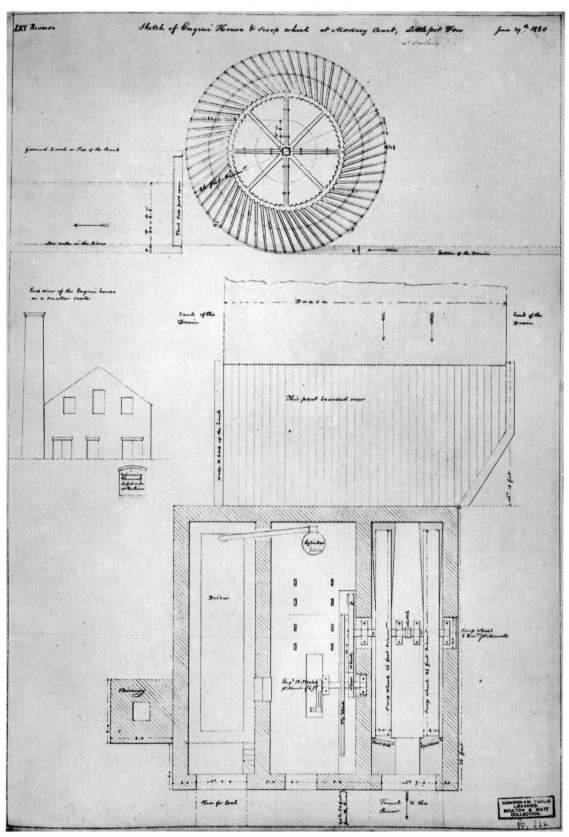

Ten Mile Bank engine, Littleport and Downham District; this was the only Fen engine to have two scoop-wheels (B. and W. Coll.)

the Littleport and Downham District, were appointed to form a Committee "to take a view of the Steam Engine near Wisbech and that the orders above written respecting the repair of mills be suspended until after this Committee have made their report on the operation of such Steam Engine".[13] Since they most probably had to go to Sutton St Edmund, which lay six miles north-west of Wisbech, their expenses were paid. Nine days later, this Committee reported that "a Steam Engine would be most beneficial to the drainage of this District",[14] and recommended a General Special Meeting of the Commissioners to be called to consider the propriety of erecting one.

At another meeting, Mr West and Messrs Hague and Topham were requested "to attend the Commissioners at Littleport on Wednesday, the first day of July next at eleven o'clock in the forenoon to enable them to inspect the waterwheel of the Mow Fen Mill in order to enable them to give their opinion as to the expediency of erecting a Steam Engine in the District".[15] Unfortunately, very little is known about Mr West. He did some other surveying for the district, but no payment appears in the Account Book. Hague and Topham were steam-engine builders from London. Eighteen Commissioners assembled at the Marquis of Granby Inn on the appropriate Wednesday, and a majority of them decided that a steam-engine would be highly beneficial to the drainage of the district. Accordingly it was ordered, on 1 July 1818,

that a Steam Engine of Thirty Horses power be immediately erected by Messrs. Hague and Topham of London, and that the same and all works incident thereto be under the Superintendance and Direction of a Committee . . . that are empowered to enter into a contract with Messrs. Hague and Topham for the erection of a steam engine of Thirty Horses power provided the expenses thereof at their manufactory or at the wharfe does not exceed one thousand eight hundred pounds, and that they accept payment for the same as follows, namely nine hundred pounds as soon as the engine is erected and the remaining sum of nine hundred pounds as soon as the engine is approved of by the said committee. . . . Ordered that Mr. West do prepare a plan and section of a waterwheel equal to the powers of the aforegoing engine.[16]

A year later, work on the engine had already commenced, for at a meeting queries were raised whether the erection of a steam-engine without the consent of the whole district was not contrary to their Act of Parliament, and also whether the present position was in fact the site which would give the most benefit to the whole district. It was finally decided that everything was in order and had been done correctly, so the officer was told to "proceed with the erection of the Steam Engine on the spot where it is now building".[17]

The engine was finished by March 1820, for on the seventh of that month payment was made to Messrs Hague and Topham of £900 as stated in the agreement. A further payment of £450 was made in July,[18] but the rest of their account was not settled until a year later, probably through shortage of money. In the following April it was decided to borrow £1,200 from a Mr Hague who had offered to lend it on the credit of the taxes, and the remaining balance was paid in June and November of 1821.[19] The debt to Mr Hague soon disappears from the Account Book, but this firm did not erect any more engines in the Fens. The sum of £1,800 would not have been the only expense in erecting this steam-engine, and probably only paid for the mechanical parts of the engine itself, with perhaps a boiler. It may not even have included the scoopwheels, as these were to be designed by Mr West, and certainly would not have covered the cost of building the engine-house. It has not been possible to isolate any figures from the Account Book which can in any way be connected with the erection of this engine, but a rough idea of the total sum involved may be gathered from the order "that the sum of Five Thousand pounds be borrowed upon the credit of the Tax".[20] It was estimated that it cost as much to build the engine-house and set the engine to work as it cost to buy the engine itself.[21] When the second engine for this district was built ten years later, the contractor was paid by the week and some of the work was carried out by local labour, so this first engine-house may have been built entirely by direct labour.

Although this engine was situated three miles south of Denver Sluice where the Ouse was not tidal, there was a considerable rise in water-level when the sluice doors were shut against the tide. The engine was fitted with two scoopwheels, although only one was in use when Rennie paid a visit

the third day after she was started. She is a Rotative Engine of 30 Horses Power, has two scoop-wheels of 26 feet diam each – one to work at high water time and two at low water – these wheels are two feet broad in the float and the one I saw at work raised against a head of water $9\frac{1}{2}$ ft and make six Revolutions p. minute – the quantity of land to be drained is 20,000 acres – but she was only considered as equal to the draining of half that quantity and another of equal horse power is proposed to be erected.[22]

Rennie was drawing up plans for the Swaffham and Bottisham engine, so he asked that Murdoch be sent by Boulton and Watt to inspect this engine. Murdoch was unlucky for the wheel-shaft had worked loose in its bearings and he did not see it at work, although he gathered that both wheels had never been used together.[23] From the absence of any complaints in the Order Book, the engine must have worked satisfactorily, but no figures can be found to show how it performed.

In 1821 a "small cottage with a blacksmith's forge was added to the steam engine"[24] and, soon after the second engine for this district was built in 1830, the earlier engine received extensive repairs. The engineer in charge of the new engine, Joseph Glynn, was asked by the Steam-Engine Committee to see what would be required to make the older engine "more effectual for the purpose of drainage",[25] and he recommended a new boiler and some other repairs. The engine worked for a further nine years until 1842, when

at a meeting of the Commissioners held on February 23 1842, when 61 were present, it was unanimously resolved that a new steam engine should be erected on the Ten Mile river, on the same spot as the first engine and in lieu thereof. . . . The construction was carried out by the Butterley Company, and that of the engine house by Goose and Dyson at a total cost of £7,100.[26]

BOROUGH FEN

Another area which adopted steam drainage after the successful application at Sutton St Edmund was the near-by Borough Fen, in part of the First District of the North Level.

The North Level of the Fens is divided into five districts. The First contains about 11,500 acres, including the Commons and is bounded on the West by the high lands of the Soke of Peterborough, from which it is separated by an ancient Roman Drain called the Carr Dyke; on the North by the River Welland, and part of a drain called the Old South Eau; and on the East and South by a ridge of high land, running from a place called the Black Horse, to the town of Eye where this ridge crosses the Carr Dyke. . . .

The water from the above five districts of low or Fen lands, containing 47,750 acres, is conveyed to Clows Cross by the Old and New South Eau, and from thence by the Shire Drain to Gunthorpe Sluice, but although the North Level drains by Clows Cross, yet the different districts of this level are very differently situated in respect to drainage.

The First District may be said to have no natural drainage because the water in the Old South Eau, at the Blackhorse, is generally higher in wet weather than the surface of the land, that is drained by it; and therefore the drainage, in great measure depends on windmills. . . .

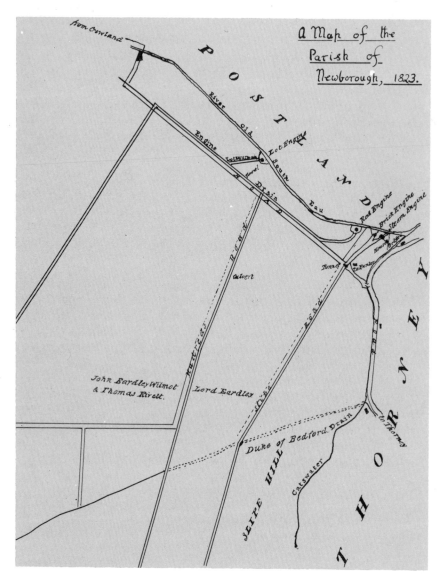

*The parish of
Newborough, 1823*

The First District is in a very different situation from all the rest. It is not only furthest from the Outfall, but it is exposed to the floods of above 12000 acres of high land, except what is intercepted by Carr Dyke.

The water that is intercepted by this drain is not properly carried off as its entrance from the Folly River into the Welland is too small; and the Folly River itself is in very bad repair, which causes the water to pass over and ouse through its banks, and over the Carr Dyke Banks, in floods, and drowns nearly the whole district. . . .[27]

The First District was the worst drained part of the North Level and it was small consolation for Borough Fen that, in spite of being part of this district and draining by the Old South Eau and the Shire Drain which were maintained by the North Level Commissioners, it was exempt from all the North Level drainage taxes.[28] Some improvement could have been obtained by straightening the existing drains, but the North Level could never have an adequate drainage until the outfall of the Nene had been improved. Rennie realized that an improvement in the Nene Outfall would enable the North Level to dispense with windmills altogether, but funds could not be raised for so great an undertaking at that time. He hoped that the North Level would join with South Holland in his plan for the whole of those areas and so "effect the complete drainage of the low lands in the North Level and in Borough Fen",[29] but the parties could not agree.

Meanwhile, Parliamentary sanction was obtained to enclose Borough Fen and improve the drainage.[30] The Commissioners decided to erect a steam-engine, for they were authorized by their Act "to erect any such Mills, Engines, and other devices (within any part of the First District) as they may think necessary for the drainage of the common".[31] This decision started an outcry from the occupiers of the other districts, led by Tycho Wing. In December 1819 he wrote to the Duke of Bedford's Auditor, W. G. Adam,

Still I should hope that the observation of "Scythens" [word illegible] with regard to the Welland Wash Embankments is applicable here, namely that the objects contemplated by the particular Act must be rendered consistent with the general safety of the Level, and it appears to me that a Steam Engine on the proposed spot for the discharge of the Boro' Fen waters would prove very injurious to the other districts of the North Level.

In still weather when there may not be sufficient wind for the Mills, the Steam Engine being constantly at work will keep up the water in the Old South Eau, and consequently in the Shire Drain. Hence it will be impossible for the other parts of the North Level to discharge any water at those times; but as the main drains all communicate at Clows Cross, the surface of the Old South Eau cannot be raised without proportionally affecting the other drains.

No mill or other engine shall be worked for throwing the waters from any part of the North Level whenever the waters in the said River Old South Eau shall be more than four feet above the level of the soil in the North Level near Whaplode Common, the same provision is made in Boro' Fen Act, para 63. In a bad state of the Outfall, when the water is held up in the Shire Drain by the sands below Gunthorpe Sluice the operation of the steam engine in still weather may keep the surface of the Old South Eau nearly if not quite at the proscribed limit; and in that case, whenever the wind may happen to blow, the Mills will be able to avail themselves but very imperfectly of the opportunity. In the present good state of the outfall, the operation of the engine might not be found very oppressive – but in other times it might be found most injurious; and we have had abundant experience that the outfall is not to be relied upon for a season.[32]

He also felt that it was most unfair that people who paid nothing towards the upkeep of the drains should in this way ruin the drainage of those who did. In addition, an evil from which they already suffered would be much increased, for there was already a considerable amount of soakage through the North Level banks, and this would be much more if the river were always kept full by the steam-engine.[33]

W. G. Adam decided to seek the advice of John Rennie, and heard from him just after Christmas. Rennie pointed out that there was insufficient fall in the drains, so that the whole of the North Level was dependent upon windmills to keep the land free from water. When the wind blew, each area had an equal chance of being drained,

but when calm, they are equally drowned. . . . If a Steam Engine or Engines is erected in one District while the windmills remain on the others, this equilibrium will be lost and the District or Districts that are to be drained by Steam Engines will have the advantage by depending for their drainage on an equable power which can work at all times whether the wind blows or not, while the others will be dependent entirely upon the wind.[34]

The conclusion he drew was that an engine of moderate size would help the windmills by pumping out water when they could not work, so there would be less water in the main drains against which the mills would have to pump when the wind did blow. But he foresaw great trouble if large engines were erected, for not only would there then be a total suspension of windmill drainage until the steam-engines had completed their task, but

such engines would prove highly injurious to the North Level and might even endanger the banks themselves. Such a state of things is to be looked at with dread, and this naturally leads me to ask whether there is any Act by which the Commissioners of any district are restrained from erecting windmills of any size or in any numbers for the drainage of those districts. . . . If there is, would not the same powers apply to the size and number of Steam Engines the Commissioners of a District could erect. . . . I fear there is only one condition that could be made in the present state of the case, namely to stipulate that before the Steam Engine or Engines are set to work, a Gauge mark should be fixed to ascertain the utmost height to which the water can be allowed to be raised in the Old South Eau and that whenever it exceeded the height of this work, it should revert again to Borough Fen.

I am decidedly of opinion that all those kind of measure tend but little towards effecting . . . a complete natural drainage while the sums of money likely to be expended upon them from time to time is great and will in a few years amount to full as much as the expense of carrying into execution some such scheme as that recommended in my report to the Bedford Level Corporation 26 January 1814.[35]

When Tycho Wing had read Rennie's letter, he was still desirous of preventing the erection of the engine if possible,[36] and began to revive Rennie's original plan for the drainage of the North Level and the Nene Outfall Cut. Towards the end of January he was still hopeful, for the Borough Fen Commissioners had not yet ordered their engine, although they had sent their "officer" to Leeds to provide himself with estimates and dimensions of steam-engines.[37] But the engine was ordered and was being built during August 1820. It was 30 h.p. and was to drain 6,000 acres.[38] Wing gives the "prime cost" as £2,500,[39] and estimated that the annual running expenses would be £320.[40] There is nothing to show what he included in his prime cost, probably only the engine itself.

There is an interesting reference to this engine in the Deeping Fen Minutes where it was "resolved that the Clerk do make application by the post of today to the Commissioners of the New Boro' Fen Drainage for permission for their Engineer to render his temporary assistance to work the steam engine at Pode Hole at such times as his duties may not be required by them".[41] The first engine to be finished at Pode Hole was the Fenton and Murray engine from Leeds, and it seems possible that the Borough Fen engine may have come from there as well.

This engine was made redundant in the same way as that at Sutton St Edmund. As early as 1828 Telford had reported to the North Level Commissioners that the whole area might have a natural drainage in consequence of the Nene Outfall Cut and the thirty windmills abandoned. The water in the River Nene ebbed out 10 feet lower than it formerly did opposite the North Level and South Holland sluices. Messrs Swansborough and Pear completed a new sluice, and in 1830 an Act was passed for a new North Level Main Drain.[42] This was cut straight from the Sluice to Clough's Cross and was only 8¼ miles in length as compared with 12 miles of the Old Shire Drain, besides being 8 feet deeper and having a capacity six times as great. At a final cost of £150,000, this work was completed in 1834 and removed the need for any mechanical drainage. Wing relates how one Sunday morning the congregation ran out of church to see the water flowing by itself in the North Level drains, something that not even the oldest of them could remember. The effect on agriculture and on the health of the inhabitants was equally startling,[43] but the engine became redundant. However, it has given its name to the little hamlet where it once stood, which is to this day called "The Engine".

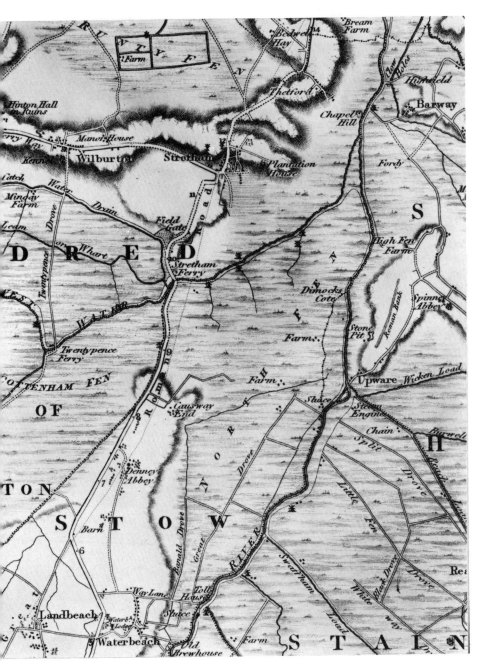

*R. G. Baker,
Map of the County
of Cambridge, 1821.
The Swaffham engine
is marked Steam
Engine, and the
Stretham engine was
built on the south
side of the river
between the first two
mills to the east of
Stretham Ferry*

SWAFFHAM AND BOTTISHAM

In the southernmost part of the Fens, plans were well advanced for building another engine which is the best known of all these early ones, for it was designed and built by John Rennie. Many people have thought that this was the first steam drainage engine in the Fens, probably based on a statement by Sir John Rennie,[44] but his father's own letter about the Ten Mile Bank engine shows that this claim is false.

Although the water-level in the Cam by Reach Lode would not be affected by the work on the Eau Brink Cut, a staunch was built at Upware under that scheme, and, as compensation for the additional soakage through the banks that this would cause, the Commissioners

83

of the Eau Brink agreed to build a new drain through the Swaffham and Bottisham District to Reach Lode at Upware. This was intended to give the area the same drainage as previously, but, because the Eau Brink Cut would carry the floods to the sea more quickly, the water would remain for a longer period each year at the normal level and the mills would drain the land more effectively. Some form of artificial drainage was still necessary because the level of the land was lower than the river.[45] The Commissioners provided themselves with a new Act of Parliament for improving the drainage by erecting "such additional Banks, Staunches, Mills, Steam Engines and other Engines thereupon for draining and conveying the water from the same",[46] and asked John Rennie for advice. In his report he pointed out

that these Fens are generally highest towards the Cam Bank on the one side and towards the high-lands in the Parishes of Swaffham and Bottisham on the other and that they are lowest in the middle. I therefore recommend that a Drain be made in the Direction of the line [in the middle] . . . to Reach Lode – there I would advise the Machinery to be placed for throwing the water into the Cam. . . . The next question is as to the Machine or Machines best adapted to raise the water into the Cam – on this subject my opinion has long been formed, namely that a Steam Engine or Engines is much preferable to any other machine. It has the advantage of always being ready to work when required, whereas windmills can only work when the wind blows and it is frequently calm when most wanted. . . . No dependence can therefore be had on Machines of this sort.[47]

Outline of the Upware engine, Swaffham and Bottisham Level (B. and W. Coll.)

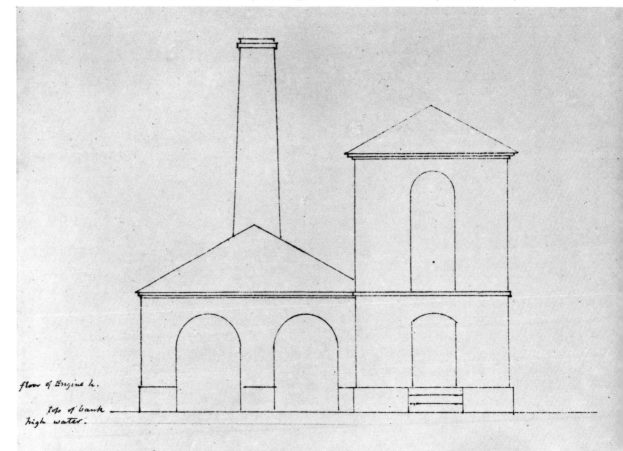

Various interior pictures of Upware engine, circa *1939 (C.O.C.)*

Far left: *The Boulton and Watt engine at Upware, looking at the governor with the fly-wheel behind (C.O.C.)*

A close-up detail of the crankpin on the Swaffham and Bottisham engine at Upware (C.O.C.)

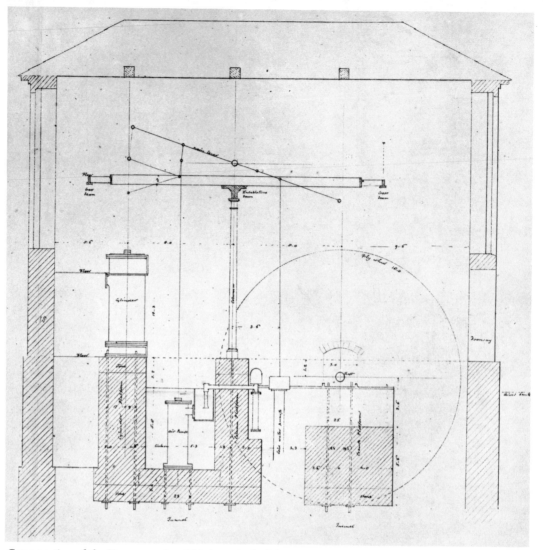

Cross-section of the Upware engine. This is typical of those engines which were constructed as part of their buildings (B. and W. Coll.)

Opposite page: *Ground-plan of the Upware engine, showing how Rennie provided for two boilers (B. and W. Coll.)*

At a meeting held at the Swan Inn, Bottisham, on 24 March 1820, the Commissioners decided to adopt Rennie's plan of drainage, but they did not have definite estimates of the cost because Rennie did not know the nature of the ground for the foundations neither had he the price of the machinery. In the meantime he wrote to Boulton and Watt, and in April he was able to give more detailed estimates based on the Ten Mile Bank engine.[48]

To drain the quantity of land in these two Parishes, which I estimate at 7,000 acres, – I imagine a Steam Engine of about Twenty Horses power will be required. This engine, including the expense of fitting it up, will cost about £1,400 – a good brick building as an Engine House and to hold the boilers, an Engine Well, and other parts belonging thereto – I can not pretend to ascertain until the ground has been examined, which Mr. Banks has undertaken to do in the course of next week; but judging from what the Engine House from the Eau Brink Cut has cost and allowing for the difference of work I should guess that about £1,600 would cover this department so that the amount of these respective articles will be about £3,600.[49]

86

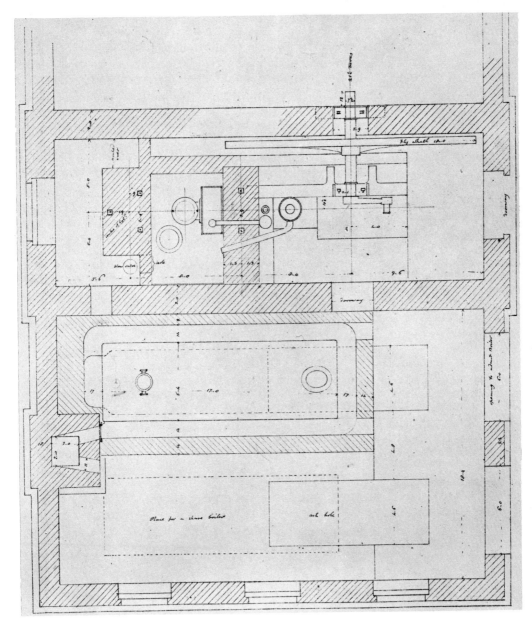

At this stage Rennie had not made final plans, nor had he settled what type of water-raising machinery the engine should drive because he was waiting for the report of William Murdoch on the Ten Mile Bank engine. Murdoch's opinion was that "when the fens are flooded nearly to the level of the river when pretty high the wheel will throw out the greatest quantity of water & therefore be preferable, but in the most general and desirable case of the water being kept down to a proper level in the ditches, a pump is best".[50] Boulton and Watt would not undertake to make the scoopwheels as these were not their line of business, so they could provide no idea of their cost but recommended that, if a rotative engine were used, it should be 24 h.p. The final decision was left to Rennie, who wrote, "I should prefer the pump, but I think it is not very probable that they would keep it in order & as the scoopwheel is quite familiar to fenmen – I believe it will be best on the whole to adopt the scoopwheel".[51]

About 12 feet below the peat surface was a strong tough yellow clay which Rennie thought capable of bearing any weight, and in January 1821 he sent an estimate of £2,288 for those parts of the engine-house above the ground.[52] Estimates for the scoopwheel races followed in April, amounting to £1,462 and another £538 would have secured a "building over the waterwheels . . . which though it would render the whole more complete may be at least for the present omitted".[53] Perhaps the Commissioners were expressing surprise at the mounting cost of their engine, but Rennie assured them that he had "reduced the prices to the lowest they can be done for".[54] The scoopwheel and gearing were built at Rennie's own works in London, and in the same letter he said that they would be sent off in a very short time so that there would be no time lost in setting the engine to work when the building was completed.[55] Then one of the Commissioners must have realized that they had not yet paid for the most important part of their pumping station, namely the scoopwheel, so Rennie replied:

I have endeavoured to ascertain as near as I can the cost of the two Spur Wheels for working the Scoop Wheel, or Wheels if a second shall be put up – the Shaft, Iron Plates, Brasses, Bolts, Scoopwheel, Water Door and Frame – all of which are nearly completed – they are all of cast iron except the float boards and will cost about £1,120 exclusive of carriage to Bottisham and of fitting in their places – the expense of this fitting I cannot pretend to estimate with any degree of correctness, but should suppose it need not exceed £100.

The building is proposed to be made for two Scoop Wheels – though when there is an abundant supply of water in the Fen and the River is flooded, one wheel will be found to be as much as the Engine can work – but it might be an advantage that a Second Scoop Wheel should be put up at a future period, which in cases of sudden falls of rain so as to fill the drains in the Fen before the River rises, the Engine in such a case would work two wheels and by thus taking the water easily out of the Fen, much expense in working the engine might be saved – For this purpose the machinery has been contrived and all that will be to do should you decide on a Second Scoop Wheel will be the shaft with the Brasses, Blocks and Scoopwheel itself – for the Spurwheel and Pinion for working the present Wheel will also work the Second Wheel, which would cost including water door about £620.[56]

The second wheel was never built, and the one that was installed was 26 feet in diameter and had forty ladles. It was felt that if a large number of ladles were used, each one would have less water to lift and so the start-posts and fixings could be made lighter.[57] The total cost of the engine would appear to be in excess of the following sum:

Steam Engine with Boiler	£1,400
Engine House	2,288
Scoopwheel House	1,462
Scoopwheel	1,120
Carriage and fitting of Scoopwheel	100
	£6,370

This does not include additional expenses such as drainwork, and is somewhat higher than the original estimate of £3,600.

DEEPING FEN

In these early areas, only small steam-engines were erected. The first large installation was in Deeping Fen, but at first the experiment was only partially successful owing to the inadequacy of the internal drains. It is not known how seriously the proposals for a steam-engine suggested by Messrs Jessop, Rennie, Maxwell and Hare were considered,[58] but certainly by 1818 the windmill drainage was insufficient and something better needed. John Rennie was again asked for his advice and he duly sent a report.

The whole of that Fen and the land draining by the same outfall, containing upwards of 40,000 Acres, is at present, I may almost say, in a lost state. . . .

The length of the Main or Vernatts Drain from Pode Hole Sluice to Vernatts Sluice is six miles, two quarters and fourteen chains, but instead of having a fall, it rises, the cill of Vernatts Sluice being one foot five inches higher than the cill of Pode Hole Sluice. So from the head of the South Drove Drain to the cill of Vernatts Sluice, a distance of fifteen miles, there is only a fall from the surface of the land of 4 feet 10 inches. . . .

Were the cill of Vernatts Sluice always clear of water, the falls I have mentioned, though small, would effect the drainage of the lands in question, though not so well as they ought to be, for a good drainage should be capable of keeping the water at least two feet under the surface of the land, but this is not the case, for there is seldom less water in the cill of Vernatts Sluice than two feet, and in ordinary floods, it is frequently four feet more, so that for many weeks together the gates of Vernatts Sluice are shut and the water accumulates in the Fen to the great injury of the lands.[59]

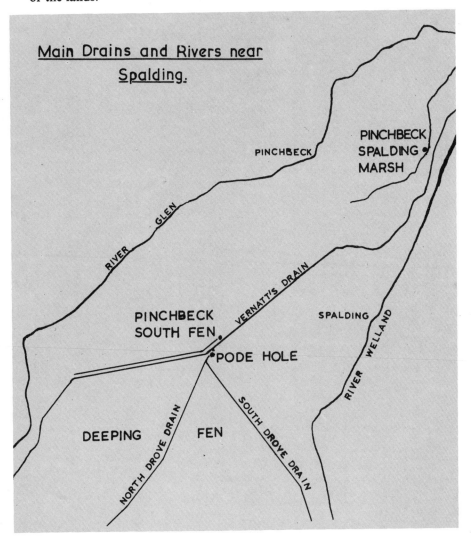

Main Drains and Rivers near Spalding

A *Pode Hole, Butterley engine, "Holland" (1825). Crankshaft, governor and flywheel (R.H.C.)*

B *Pode Hole, Fenton and Murray engine, "Kesteven" A view of the governor, connecting-rod and flywheel (R.H.C.)*

C *Pode Hole, Fenton and Murray engine, "Kesteven" Looking up towards the beam with the piston valves and cylinder in the background (R.H.C.)*

Beam of Kesteven engine. This is a single casting (Deeping Fen I.D.B.)

The remedy that Rennie suggested was to extend the Vernatt's Drain by a new cut so that it would empty into the River Witham, or at least extend the drain farther seawards, but this scheme was far too expensive and the money could not be raised owing to an agricultural depression prevailing at the time.[60] Therefore, the Commissioners considered building steam-engines, but the opinion of Counsel was given that the Trustees for the Fen were not authorized to erect a steam-engine on the Vernatt's Drain. So Thomas Pear was asked to make a report on the building and running expenses of a steam-engine situated on the Hill's Drain at the other end of the district to pump into the Welland above Spalding.[61] He decided that "the advantages to be derived from erecting an engine at the point proposed would be extremely imperfect and ineffectual, and it would be better to abandon the same".[62] Three hundred copies of this report were printed, but all of them seem to have disappeared.

Further advice was sought from Rennie, who, since funds could not be raised for his earlier scheme, held the opinion that steam-engines would be the next best measure and recommended that they should be placed where the North and South Drove drains joined the Vernatt's Drain.

The size of the Steam Engines is not easy to calculate, because the rain that falls is not regular through out the year. . . . I cannot however calculate that less than One Hundred and Twenty Horses power would be at all likely to be effectual, perhaps a larger power would be adviseable and as the extra expense would be but trivial – I submit this point for consideration.

If One Hundred and Twenty horses power is adopted, Two engines of Sixty Horses each will be most suitable – as in case of accident to one, the other will be able to perform her work and one set of duplicate articles will suffice in place of two which would be necessary were the engines to be of different sizes.

It is not in my power to say what period each year these engines will be required to work – but I should expect that three months would be the utmost. Now if working to their full power they will consume about Ten Tons of good Newcastle Coal per day, which, taking the coals at £1. 5/– p. Ton, will be £12. 10/–, and if to this is added Engine Keepers, Tear and Wear, Oil Tallow etc., it may be reckoned at £16. 10/– p. day – if the engines work ninety days in the year to their full powers, this will be £1,485, say £1,500, but if fewer days it will be less in proportion.

In regard to the cost of the Engines and buildings I have recommended, – I cannot venture to speak with accuracy unless I were to visit the place and make out correct Drawings, of all that is to be done, but I apprehend I shall not err much if I state the Engines and their Buildings at £20,000. Should you decide upon larger engines than those I have mentioned, the expense of erection will not be materially increased and unless there is more work to perform, the consumption of fuel will not be encreased.

There is now a Steam Engine erecting for the drainage of Bottisham and Swaffham Fens, which together are about Five Thousand Eight Hundred Acres, the water from which will have to be raised in floods in the Cam about eight feet – This Engine is Twenty Four Horses power, which is about the same proportional power as that I have calculated for Deeping Fen, but if any considerable portion of the water from the Counter Drain is likely to be raised by the Engines, I would submit whether a less power should be adopted than One Hundred and Sixty Horses, i.e. two engines of Eighty Horses each. The extra cost of erecting them would not exceed £2,000, while the consumption of Coals, Tear, Wear, Engine men, would be the same if no more water was to be raised.[63]

But nothing could be done until the legal position had been clarified, and in the meantime Rennie's death in 1821 prevented his supervision of the erection of these engines. A new Act was obtained from Parliament, enabling the drainage rates to be raised and steam-engines to be built at Pode Hole where the North and South Drove drains joined Vernatt's Drain.[64]

On 23 July 1823 Benjamin Bevan was appointed Civil Engineer for Deeping Fen and made responsible for the erection of the engines authorized by Parliament. In August he applied for authority to contract for two 60 h.p. engines at something less than £2,000 each and also all the other requisite materials needed for their construction,[65] but permission was temporarily withheld because there were 3,500 additional acres of very low ground which might have to be drained by the engines. It was not until October that Mr Bevan was given authority to contract for two engines, one of 80 h.p. and the other of 60 h.p. with duplicates of those parts which were most likely to be damaged by accidents.[66] There was a delay in starting building because the land where the engines were to be erected was owned by Mr Adam Gressam, who would not agree to sell it until March 1824. Work on the foundations was begun in May, when Mr Bevan gave the Trustees "an assurance that although he was not satisfied with the progress which had hitherto taken place in driving the piles for the foundations, yet he felt no reasonable doubt that both engines would be brought into complete operation by Xmas".[67]

Mr Bevan finally ordered the engines from different firms. The 60 h.p. one came from Fenton and Murray of Leeds, and the 80 h.p. from the Butterley Company near Derby. Not even the Trustees knew whether "there was any difference in the contract between the two engines from Leeds and Butterley",[68] and Mr Bevan has left no records of his transactions. Neither engine was ready to work by Christmas 1824, when he made some explanations about the capacity of the waterways and the strength of the buildings, and also stated that he hoped that the Leeds engine would be ready to start in the course of about six weeks.[69] The delay seems to have been caused by the Butterley Company who were making both scoopwheels besides one engine, for in April Joseph Simpson was sent to Butterley to find out the cause of the delay in delivery.[70] It would seem that the Leeds engine was working by June, but some of the parts for the Butterley engine had still not arrived.[71] Mr Bevan caused great inconvenience by not attending at the engine, but almost all the work was completed by August. In that month Mr Mawson from Leeds was appointed Engineer of both steam-engines at a salary of £200 per annum, with his house, garden and coal free, but he had to find his own labourers.[72]

The engines had been working for a sufficient time before the New Year for complaints to be lodged that they were stopped when the water was too high in the Fen.[73] It was therefore resolved that they should be worked at night if the occasion demanded.[74] Not everything was finished and the Butterley Company was not paid until November 1826 because they had not fitted a governor to their engine.[75] Unfortunately, Mr Mawson did not properly attend to his job, for the Trustees examined the state of the engines and expressed their dissatisfaction with the condition in which they found them. Mr Mawson was dismissed after little more than a year in his post. Mr John Trickett "who had fitted the machinery to both engines and put up the Butterley Engine"[76] was employed in his stead.

Rennie's estimate of £20,000 for these engines was considerably more accurate than that for the Swaffham and Bottisham engine. At the end of the financial year in April 1825 the account for the engines stood as follows:

	£ s. d.
Expenses obtaining Act of Parliament,	£ 2062. 4. 7.
Purchase of land for site of Engines,	210. 4. 0.
Wm. Tubb for bricks,	720. 16. 0.
Payments to Officers,	225. 12. 1.
Civil Engineers Expenditure to this day,	10642. 5. 6.
Already paid,	£13861. 2. 2.
Balance due from Trustees,	
By Mr. Wade, Stone Merchant,	176. 8. 9.
By Manufacturers of the Leeds Engine,	127. 6. 0.
The whole of the Butterley Company Engine had to be paid for which he estimated would cost not exceeding £3,300 including the putting up of the same,	3300. 0. 0.
The Account will therefore stand as follows	£17464. 16. 11.
Independent of the above charges, the Engine House and Works at Pode Hole,	1700. 0. 0.
Joseph Simpsons estimate of repairs and deepening the North and South Drove Drains	4408. 0. 0.
Vernatts Drain Banks,	500. 0. 0.
Cross Drain,	600. 0. 0.
Contingencies,	2000. 0. 0.
	£9208. 16. 0.[77]

The total bill for all the works connected with the erection of the steam-engines came to an estimated sum of £26,673. These two engines together formed the largest fen pumping station for many years to come and their performance and further history will be covered later.

The March Fourth District, or West Fen, had a 40 h.p. engine built for them by the Butterley Company in 1826. It was the usual single-cylinder condensing beam-engine, draining about 3,600 acres[78] by means of a 28 foot diameter scoopwheel, 2 feet 9 inches wide, discharging 70 tons a minute.[79] Joseph Glynn may have designed and erected this engine, but it has not been possible to trace the records for this district.

The engine worked well and the proprietors received great benefit, but they failed to properly estimate the costs and they found their taxes were not adequate to meet the charges. They had to apply to Parliament for another Act to increase the taxes to enable them to continue working their engine.[80] They were given permission to borrow up to £5,000, a sum that indicates how much they had already spent, and to raise an additional rate or assessment of up to 6s. per acre per annum, an amount necessary to pay running expenses and leave a little over to service the debt and pay off the mortgage. Later the tax was 5s. per annum.[81]

Although it has been stated that this engine ceased working in 1900,[82] the people living next door said that it stopped working around 1940 when the boiler failed. As a temporary measure, the engine was taken out of gear and a large traction-engine coupled to the scoopwheel. Even with the "slacker" at the drain side of the wheel closed right down so very little water could reach it, the traction-engine could only just manage the load. Now the water is pumped out from the other end of the district so the machinery has been entirely removed and the scoopwheel-pit filled in.

PINCHBECK SOUTH FEN

Pinchbeck South Fen lies to the north of Deeping Fen and contains about 1,700 acres. Although it was originally administered as the Fourth District by the Trustees of Deeping Fen and is so again today, at this period it was a separate unit lying on the other side of Vernatt's Drain from the rest of Deeping Fen. There was a tunnel between the two under Vernatt's Drain, so the people of Pinchbeck South Fen asked the Trustees of Deeping Fen whether they could drain some of their water by the tunnel to the steam-engines at Pode Hole. The Deeping Fen Trustees agreed to this, providing the expenses were paid, and a bill was sent on 9 April 1828 made out as follows:

28 Chaldrons of Coals at 30/–,	£42. 0. 0.
Oil and Tallow,	4. 0. 0.
Engineers Allowance and Labour,	9. 0. 0.
Superintendents Allowance and Labour,	3. 18. 0.
	£58. 18. 0.[83]

The Deeping Fen Trustees seem to have been determined to make a profit out of their smaller neighbours, for that year they had paid, on average, only 28s. per chaldron of coals. Then the rates were raised higher, and a demand made for "£20 per day for the running of the Engines during such time as the waters of the said District shall run to the Engines through the said tunnel" and also for the Fourth District to "deposit the sum of two hundred pounds to be answerable for the said expenses and any damages which the Trustees may sustain by complying with the progress of this petition".[84] But worse was to come, for when the Fourth District suggested a complete integration with Deeping Fen, they were asked to pay a lump sum of £4,500 by 6 July 1830,[85] to pay the same taxes as

94

the other districts, and in addition to continue paying their own internal taxes for the upkeep of their banks and ditches. This price was too high, and they "decided they could not accede to such conditions",[86] and set about building their own engine which cost only £3,000.[87] This engine was situated opposite to the others at Pode Hole and also pumped into the Vernatt's Drain. Although it worked until after 1896,[88] no traces now remain.

HUNDRED FOOT ENGINE

It was decided at a meeting of the Commissioners for the Littleport and Downham District held on 27 November 1828 to erect a second steam pumping station on the bank of the Hundred Foot River near the Westmoor double-lift mills. A Committee was appointed and empowered to enter into contracts for the "erection of such engine and all the incidentals thereto appertaining".[89] First of all it was necessary to obtain permission from the Bedford Level Corporation to use the foreland by the Hundred Foot River for the building, and also to cut through the barrier bank to build a tunnel for the discharge water. The Clerk was ordered to write to Mr Dyson, the Engineer to the Bedford Level, to come and see where they intended to erect their engine so he could represent them when their petition was read at the next meeting of the Corporation.[90] Leave was duly granted "to erect the engine on the foreland of the bank as required by the Commissioners paying to the Corporation an acknowledgement of one shilling per annum and having a lease thereof for the term of ninety nine years and that the said Commissioners have also leave to cut through the Great Bank".[91]

At the Annual Meeting of the Littleport and Downham Commissioners in April 1829, the Steam-Engine Committee made the following report:

The Committee first directed their attention to the spot whereon it would be desirable the said engine should be erected and thought it proper to call in to their assistance Mr. Jos. Glynn, a Civil Engineer, whose opinion coincided with their own namely that the back foreland of the 100 Foot Bank immediately below the Westmoor Mills was as eligible a situation as could be obtained consistent with the order of the Commissioners.

The next object of the Committee was to ascertain of what power the said engine should be in order the most effectually to answer the purpose of Draining the District on which point they also thought proper to consult the said Engineer and after mature consideration your Committee came to the determination that an engine of less than 80 horses would be inadequate for the purposes intended in as much as they conceived that it would be far better to have a little power too much than want any. The preliminary points being arranged, your Committee to prevent loss of time next authorised your Officer to procure a sufficient quantity of proper piles for the foundation, most of which they understand are already on the spot – they also advertised for, and received tenders for 300,000 good sound bricks to be used in the erection of the Engine House and other necessary buildings and agreed with several parties for the same to be delivered on the spot before mentioned at 35/– per thousand.

Your Committee have also commenced the drain work which they deemed absolutely necessary to supply the intended engine with sufficient water according to her powers.

Lastly upon your Committee anxiously considering the serious and important works committed to their charge acted with the greatest caution as to the Engineer to be employed upon the occasion and accordingly made numerous applications where they conceived most likely to obtain the desired information. At length Mr. Glynn Civil Engineer on behalf of the Butterley Company personally applied for the contract furnishing many indisputable references as to his capability and responsibility – your Committee however thought proper to apply to Mr. Mylne and Sir Edward Banks from both of whom they received the highest testimonials of his abilities and your Committee also took upon themselves the responsibility of sending three of their number to inspect similar engines erected by the said Company at March and Spalding every part of which

Hundred Foot engine from the drain side, circa *1900* (*C.O.C.*)

Front of Hundred Foot scoopwheel, circa *1900* (*C.O.C.*)

highly gratified them and ratified the opinions of Mr. Mylne and Sir Edward Banks – your Committee therefore being fully assured of the capability of the said Engineer have agreed to contract with the Butterley Company for an Engine of 80 Horses power at the sum of £4,000 – your Committee further beg to observe that they have obtained leave of the Honourable Corporation of the Bedford Level to erect the said Engine on the foreland. . . .[92]

The report was approved and confirmed, and a contract signed with Charles Briggs to build the engine-house. He was paid weekly and received the first sum on 18 June 1829.[93] The foundation was very bad, there being 7 yards in depth of black peat above the clay so that 600 piles were driven into the clay with 3-inch deals laid close together and spiked down to form a complete floor so that if any settlement took place the whole would sink equally.[94] The last weekly payment to Briggs was made on 29 April 1830, and in May he received the balance of his account which came to a total of £2,574 15s. 6d.[95] The Butterley Company was paid £4,000 in the same April, so the engine cost £6,574, exclusive of bricks and piles, work for deepening the drains, and expenses for supervisory engineers.

No record was kept of when the engine first worked, but it must have been running by some time in April because complaints were made in the Annual Meeting at the end of that month. It was decided to ask Mr Mylne:

to inspect the Engine and to advise the Commissioners on the following points,
1) Whether the engine is of 80 Horse Power and delivers the full quantity of water it ought to deliver.
2) Whether the waterwheel is so constructed and placed as to enable the engine to work with the greatest advantage to the District.
3) Whether he can suggest any alterations in the construction or position of the wheel or of the waterways.
4) Whether he considers the machinery of the engine in any way defective.[96]

Mylne reported favourably, although the engine incorporated a peculiar feature designed to take advantage of the tidal river into which it pumped. The scoopwheel could be worked at two different speeds. It was

35 feet in diameter, and with its axis and toothed wheel work on it weighed 54 tons. There was a sliding pinion on the engine axis, 4 feet in diameter, weighing 33 cwt., and turning at 13 R.P.M. At high tide, this engaged with a wheel of 24 feet diam., with internal teeth, giving the ladles a velocity of 212 ft. p. min. and discharging 21,980 gallons of water. At low tide, the pinion, by help of machinery, is made to slide into action with another wheel of 16 ft. diam., discharging 32,880 gallons of water.[97]

This wheel was enlarged by lengthening the ladles to a diameter of 41 feet 8 inches, and at some time the double gearing removed, perhaps when the wheel was replaced in 1882 by one of 50 feet in diameter, the largest in the Fens, when other alterations were also carried out.

WALDERSEA DISTRICT

Waldersea District contains about 6,500 acres of fenland lying on the east bank of the River Nene just south of Wisbech. Unfortunately, no records can be found, for the history would be interesting as the drainage was originally started during the reign of James I.[98] In spite of many windmills, some privately owned by farmers to pump the water from their lands into the Main Drain, and others set up by the Commissioners to clear the Main Drain, "previous to the erection of the powerful steam engine, . . . at certain periods of the year, boats went over the land, which was the habitation of wildfowl".[99]

The Commissioners, realizing that the Nene Outfall Cut would not materially improve their drainage because they were above the town of Wisbech, decided to apply to Parliament for a new Act. By it they were authorized to borrow up to £8,000 and set up an "Engine or Engines for the Purposes of the said Drainage, the same shall be worked by Steam only".[100] The existing large windmills were to be taken down and sold if they were no longer wanted, and the little mills, or those which were privately owned, were to be taken down after three years had expired if the drainage by the steam-engine had been sufficiently perfected.[101]

Because the River Nene was tidal at the place where the Waldersea Main Drain flowed into it, the steam-engine that was erected in 1832 worked a bucket-pump and not a scoop-wheel. Although windmills sometimes drove this type of pump for draining small areas, it it believed that this was the only steam-driven example in the Great Level of the Fens. They were not popular because the valves and working parts became blocked with mud and reed which found their way into the inlet.[102] This pump was 6 feet in diameter, and lifted 46 barrels of water each stroke, making from 6 to 10 strokes per minute, according to the height of tide in the river.[103] In 1 minute it raised 63 tons of water,[104] from 10 to 20 feet, the lift at low water being about 8 feet.[105]

The engine had a cylinder of 40 inches diameter by 8 feet stroke, developing 60 h.p., and with the buildings cost about £3,000.[106] If this figure for the erection costs is correct, then it was the cheapest engine in the Fens for its horse-power. It appears to have done its work well, for "immediately after the erection . . . the lands were laid dry and splendid crops of

Far left: *Waldersea engine with later additions (E.J.A.K.)*

Valve gear of Marton engine on the Trent. This was a Cornish-type pump engine like the one originally installed at Waldersea (R.H.C.)

corn grown the first year. I went over this land just after a flood, and the lands were as dry as any in the country."[107] The cost of coal worked out at about £150 per annum and the drainage tax was 4s. 6d. per acre per annum, which, as soon as the mortgage had been paid off, would be reduced to 1s. 6d.

WATERBEACH LEVEL

Two of these early beam-engines have been preserved. The earlier and larger, the Stretham engine in the Waterbeach Level, was built in 1831, eighteen years after Rennie's recommendation that a steam-engine should be used in this area. He showed that there was no hope of these lands ever obtaining a natural drainage because they were lower than the adjacent rivers, and he thought that "the best mode of Artificial Drainage will be by a Steam Engine in place of Windmills".[108] He pointed out that the steam-engine would always be ready to work and this would prevent the land being flooded, "an advantage which to Agriculturalists requires no encomium of mine. The value of the land will be very much encreased, I presume in a far greater degree than the extra cost of working the Steam Engine over that of Windmills."[109] The snag lay in the expense of the scheme, for there was not only the steam-engine with its main drain to consider, but Rennie recommended a catchwater drain to exclude water from the highlands surrounding this Fen. The cost was too great, for the catchwater drain alone would have cost £4,838 and the whole scheme £15,000. The steam-engine itself was expected to cost £5,750 and would have worked a pump and not a scoopwheel. To the Commissioners who were already afraid that their

Stretham engine from the river side (E.J.A.K.)

existing debt of £2,000 was too large, these sums were astronomical, for they had to consider the running expenses as well.

The expense of working the Steam Engine is not easy to compute as it depends entirely upon the quantity of rain that falls annually and on the proportion of what does fall, that is consumed in Evaporation and in the supply of vegetation, also on what soaks through the banks of the Ouse and Cam, but as far as I can judge the whole consumption of fuel including the expense of Engine Working, and repairs of Machinery is not likely to exceed £700 p. Annum, which is not quite 3/8 p. acre.[110]

There the matter remained until 1829 when Joseph Glynn was requested to go over the Level and ascertain the best situation to erect a steam-engine.[111] It was not until June 1831 that a meeting was held to consider several tenders, from which one submitted by Joseph Glynn was accepted for building a steam-engine for £2,900.[112] A month later the tender of Mr Briggs of West Ferry, Lincolnshire, for £2,050 was accepted for building the engine-house. These were the same two firms which built the Hundred Foot engine, but here there was no need to drive piles for the foundations because there was a bed of hard concrete gravel that lay about 10 feet below the surface. In the contract for building the engine-house there was a penalty clause which stated that the building was to be finished by 1 December 1831, or a forfeit of £10 per day would be incurred. Since there is no mention that this ever had to be applied, the building was presumably completed by that date and the engine working about then.

Beam of Stretham engine. This consists of two parallel beams bolted together 11 inches apart (E.J.A.K.)

Top of cylinder, Stretham engine (E.J.A.K.)

of piston-rod and
for Watts
llel Motion,
ham engine
A.K.)

Air pump bucket, with top removed, in condenser of Stretham engine (E.J.A.K.)

Pinchbeck Spalding Marsh. From left to right the doors are coalyard, boiler-house, engine-house and scoopwheel (E.J.A.K.)

PINCHBECK, SPALDING MARSH

The other engine that is still preserved is near Pinchbeck. Either because there was more seepage through the banks of Vernatt's Drain from the water pumped into it by the Deeping Fen engines, or because the outfall of the River Welland deteriorated still further, the Commissioners of this district found they needed better drainage. They resorted to an Act of Parliament which authorized them to

make, erect and build on the said *Blue Gowt* Drain, at a certain place called *Stickworth Gowt*, in the said Parish of Pinchbeck, one or more good and substantial Engine or Engines, to be worked by steam or otherwise, with all proper Machinery, Houses, Sluices, Pits and other necessary Works, and also to improve the said Blue Gowt Drain.[113]

The outfall of the Blue Gowt Drain, which it shares with the Vernatt's Drain into the Welland, was obstructed so that the land was "very wet until the engine was built in 1832, and great numbers of sheep caught the rot; it is now a beautiful district of good rich land, of clay and silt containing between 4,000 and 5,000 acres".[114]

The engine that was erected by the Trustees in 1833 was a low-pressure condensing beam-engine, 20 n.h.p., driving a scoopwheel of 24 feet diameter and 2 feet 2 inches wide, the scoops being 5 feet long. The wheel made 7 revolutions to 28 of the engine and worked against an average head of 5 to 6 feet, rising to 8 feet in floods.[115] The engine is a self-contained unit, built with "A" frames on a cast-iron bedplate, a method which was quite adequate for small engines. It has the distinction of being the last steam-driven scoopwheel to work in the Fens, for it was not replaced by any other form of pump until 1952 when the boiler became unsafe for further use.[116]

NOTES

1. J. Rennie, Letter Books, vol. 7, p. 432, 23 February 1814.
2. B.L.C., London, 18 August 1664.
3. T. Wing, *Considerations on the Principles of Mr. Rennie's Plans for the Drainage of the North Level ...* (1820), p. 22.
4. ibid.
5. Littleport and Downham Order Book, 12 May 1818.
6. ibid., 21 May 1818.
7. B. and W. Coll., Watt to W. Swansborough, 6 and 18 August 1814.
8. 57 Geo. III, c. 69.
9. S. Wells, *The History of the Drainage of ... Bedford Level* (1830).
10. R. G. Baker, Map of the County of Cambridgeshire and the Isle of Ely, 19 July 1821.
11. W. H. Wheeler, *The History of the Fens of South Lincolnshire* (2nd ed. 1897).
12. J. A. Clarke, "The Great Level of the Fens", *J.R.A.S.*, vol. 8 (1847), p. 102.
13. Littleport and Downham Order Book, 12 May 1818.
14. ibid., 21 May 1818.
15. ibid., 17 June 1818.
16. ibid., 1 July 1818.
17. ibid., 22 July 1819.
18. Littleport and Downham Account Book, 7 March and 24 July 1820.
19. ibid., 9 June (two entries) and 16 November 1821.
20. Littleport and Downham Order Book, 16 April 1820.
21. A. Young, *A. of A.*, vol. 44, 22 July 1800.
22. B. and W. Coll., from J. Rennie, 28 March 1820.
23. ibid., Watt to J. Rennie, 30 June 1820.
24. Littleport and Downham Order Book, 25 April 1821.
25. ibid., 24 April 1833.
26. *Presentation to Joseph Martin, 1909.*
27. J. Rennie, Letter Books, vol. 6, p. 25, 17 June 1809.
28. T. Wing, Letter Books, 4 December 1819.
29. J. Rennie, Letter Books, vol. 7, p. 411, 26 January 1814.
30. 52 Geo. III, c. 143, extended by 59 Geo. III, c. 77.
31. T. Wing, Letter Books, 4 December 1819.
32. ibid.
33. ibid., 20 December 1819.
34. J. Rennie, Letter Books, vol. 10, p. 417, 27 December 1819.
35. ibid.
36. T. Wing, Letter Books, 9 January 1820.
37. ibid., 24 January 1820.
38. T. Wing, *Considerations on the Principles of Mr. Rennie's Plans for the Drainage of the North Level ...* (1820), p. 22.
39. T. Wing, Letter Books, 1 February 1820.
40. T. Wing, *Considerations on the Principles of Mr. Rennie's Plans for the Drainage of the North Level ...* (1820), p. 22.
41. Deeping Fen Minutes, 7 June 1825.
42. T. Telford, *Life of Thomas Telford* (1838), p. 119.
43. ibid., p. 322.
44. Sir J. Rennie, *Autobiography ...* (1875), p. 160.
45. J. Rennie, Letter Books, vol. 11, p. 28, 2 February 1820.
46. 59 Geo. III, c. 78.
47. J. Rennie, Letter Books, vol. 11, pp. 31–3, 2 February 1820.
48. B. and W. Coll., Watt to J. Rennie, 11 April 1820.
49. J. Rennie, Letter Books, vol. 11, p. 122, 13 April 1820.
50. B. and W. Coll., Watt to J. Rennie, 30 June 1820.
51. ibid., from J. Rennie, 14 July 1820.
52. J. Rennie, Letter Books, vol. 11, p. 182, 9 January 1821.
53. ibid., vol. 12, p. 55, 5 April 1821.
54. ibid.

55. ibid.
56. ibid., p. 67, 16 April 1821.
57. B. and W. Coll., John Walker to William Murdoch, 15 and 21 November 1820.
58. J. Rennie, Letter Books, vol. 2, p. 199, 11 August 1800.
59. ibid., vol. 10, p. 6, 16 October 1818.
60. ibid., vol. 11, p. 340, 6 December 1820.
61. Deeping Fen Minutes, 29 June 1820.
62. ibid., 22 August 1820.
63. J. Rennie, Letter Books, vol. 11, p. 342, 6 December 1820.
64. 4 Geo. IV, c. 76.
65. Deeping Fen Minutes, 26 August 1823.
66. ibid., 9 October 1823.
67. ibid., 10 May 1824.
68. ibid., 13 February 1826.
69. ibid., 20 December 1824.
70. ibid., 13 April 1825.
71. ibid., 4 July 1825.
72. ibid., 4 August 1825.
73. ibid., 2 January 1826.
74. ibid., 13 February 1826.
75. ibid., 27 November 1826.
76. ibid., 27 February 1827.
77. Deeping Fen Account Book, 7 April 1825.
78. J. Glynn, "Draining Land by Steam Power", *Trans. Soc. of Arts*, vol. 51 (1838), p. 11.
79. J. M. Heathcote, *Scoopwheel and Centrifugal Pump* (1877), p. 4.
80. 9 Geo. IV, c. 40.
81. J. A. Clarke, op. cit., p. 98.
82. R. H. Clark, "Early Engines of the Eastern Counties", *English Mechanics*, 29 May 1936.
83. Deeping Fen Minutes, 9 April 1828.
84. ibid., 6 August 1828.
85. ibid., 9 June 1829.
86. ibid.
87. J. A. Clarke, "On the Farming of Lincolnshire", *J.R.A.S.*, vol. 12 (1851), p. 324.
88. W. H. Wheeler, op. cit., p. 120.
89. Littleport and Downham Order Book, 27 November 1828.
90. ibid., 1 April 1829.
91. B.L.C., Minute Book, 16 April 1829.
92. Littleport and Downham Order Book, 29 April 1829.
93. Littleport and Downham Account Book, 18 June 1829.
94. J. Glynn, op. cit., p. 16.
95. Littleport and Downham Account Book, computed from figures given between June 1829 and May 1830.
96. Littleport and Downham Order Book, 28 April 1830.
97. J. Glynn, op. cit., p. 16.
98. 4 Jam. I, c. 13.
99. S. Jonas, "On the Farming of Cambridgeshire", *J.R.A.S.*, vol. 7 (1846), p. 69.
100. 9 Geo. IV, c. 89.
101. ibid.
102. W. H. Wheeler, *The Drainage of Fens* . . . (1888), p. 50.
103. S. Jonas, op. cit., p. 64.
104. J. A. Clarke, "The Great Level of the Fens", *J.R.A.S.*, vol. 8 (1847), p. 105.
105. L. Gibbs, "Pumping Machinery in the Fenland and by the Trent-side", *Min. Proc. Inst. Civ. Eng.*, vol. XCIV (1888), p. 264.
106. S. Jonas, op. cit., p. 64.
107. ibid.
108. J. Rennie, Letter Books, vol. 8, p. 22, 5 March 1814.
109. ibid.
110. ibid.
111. Waterbeach Level Order Book, 29 May 1829.

112. ibid., 29 June 1831.
113. 2 Wil. IV, c. 95.
114. J. A. Clarke, "The Great Level of the Fens", *J.R.A.S.*, vol. 8 (1847), p. 121.
115. W. H. Wheeler, *The History of the Fens of South Lincolnshire* (2nd ed. 1897), p. 118.
116. See A. Bloom, *The Fens* (1953), for an account of a visit to this engine while it was still working.

CHAPTER VIII

Unlimited, Untiring Power

These first steam-engines in the Fens followed the pattern of design customary for that period. They were single vertical-cylinder low-pressure condensing beam-engines, massively built, so many worked for over a hundred years. Inside the engine-house, the scene was dominated by the large connecting-rod that hung vertically from a slot in the ceiling. At Waldersea this was directly joined to the pump under the floor which raised the water into the river, but where a scoopwheel was installed, the connecting-rod worked a crank. Against the wall nearest the scoopwheel was the flywheel which was keyed on to the crankshaft, and was used to bar the engine round by hand. On the crankshaft was also keyed a gear-wheel which drove the scoopwheel. The gears might be inside the engine-house as they were at the Ten Mile Bank engine, but later they were fitted inside the scoop-wheel-pit. In the middle of the engine-house, pillars rose from the floor to support the entablature which carried the main bearings for the beam. At Upware in the Swaffham and Bottisham engine, this was decorated with classical motifs, and at other engines many of the iron castings were highly ornamented.

Beyond the pillars was the steam-cylinder. This might be on the same level as the crank-shaft, as at Swaffham, or on a slightly higher floor as at Stretham, because underneath was the condenser tank which had to be above the level of the drain. At the base of the cylinder were the levers and valves for starting the engine, once it had been barred round to the correct position. From here stairs led up to the top of the cylinder where there was a platform so that the engine-man could easily reach the valves and piston for maintenance and packing. Another flight of stairs went up to the beam landing. At one end, the beam was coupled to the piston-rod by Watt's parallel motion, and at the other it was joined directly to the connecting-rod. Since all these bearings had to be oiled, many engines were built with no protective railing round the beam, so there was nothing to guard the engine-man from a drop of 20 feet or more to the lower crankshaft floor. Some of the smaller engines, such as Pinchbeck, were built with the same type of layout, but the engine and beam were supported on cast-iron frames. This enabled them to be self-supporting and not built as an integral part of their houses. Small iron platforms were fitted instead of floors, on which the engine-men could stand for oiling and maintenance. This helped to reduce the size of the engine-house and lower the cost.

The engines and boilers contained many very heavy iron castings which, besides the enormous weight of the scoopwheel, needed good solid foundations. Rennie was unwilling to give a firm estimate for building the Swaffham and Bottisham engine until he had ascertained what lay beneath the peat. He asked that the nature of the ground should be determined either by digging a hole 12 to 14 feet deep or by a trial bore.[1] He was lucky to find good clay at a depth of about 12 feet, for in many places the peat went much deeper. Therefore, it is not surprising to find that advantage was taken of a firm subsoil, even if it meant that the engine might not be sited in the best place. At both the Waterbeach Level and the Magdalen Fen engines, the foundations were built on a "natural bed of concrete gravel . . . which lay at an accessible depth from the surface".[2] Otherwise the only way of obtaining an adequate foundation was by driving piles and placing cross-timbers on top of

The Chear Fen engine was built by the same maker as the Smithey Fen engine and this picture is taken from almost the same place (R.H.C.)

Smithey Fen engine taken from the floor by the top of the cylinder (R.H.C.)

Connecting-rod and flywheel of the Benwick engine. The "A" frame supporting the beam can be seen in the background (R.H.C.)

Watt's Parallel Motion on the Over engine (R.H.C.)

Valve chest and cylinder of the left hand grasshopper engine at W. Butterwick on the W. bank of the R. Trent (R.H.C.)

A view along the beam of the Stow Bridge engine (R.H.C.)

Whittington engine, showing the very ornate castings of the supporting frames (R.H.C.)

Cylinder of the Whittington engine (R.H.C.)

them. This was done at Pode Hole for the Deeping Fen engines, and also for the Hundred Foot engine as well as many others. The driving of 600 piles at the Hundred Foot engine must have been an undertaking of some magnitude before the general introduction of the steam pile-driver.

These engines were housed in brick buildings which were divided into three sections to contain the different parts. There was a shed or house for the scoopwheel, and a separate room for the engine so it was not damaged by the spray from the wheel or the steam from the boilers which were in a third compartment. In addition, there might be a smithy or workshop and perhaps a shed for coal. In smaller engines these could be contained under one roof. Examples of this kind were the Ten Mile Bank engine and March West and Pinchbeck engine. For larger engines this would have entailed a great waste of space and added to the cost, because the boiler-house did not need to be as high or as strong as the engine-house. Rennie's design for the Swaffham and Bottisham engine takes advantage of using a lower roof for the boiler-house, and this idea was developed by Glynn into a standard design of engine and buildings which was built all over the Fens. The first of these was the Hundred Foot engine, and the Stretham engine was of the same type, only the reverse way round. This design was used in over a dozen engines built during a period of fifteen years, and examples still remain, but bereft of their engines, at Mepal and Binnimore near March. There were improvements in details, but many of the parts were standardized, which must have helped to reduce the expense.

Some of the details of how these engines were constructed are contained in the Agreement between the Waterbeach Level Commissioners and Charles Briggs who built the

Stretham engine-house.[3] The foundations were to be carried down to "the hard solid Stratum supposed to be about eleven and a half feet below the surface of the land". The building was to be of brick, "to ground level, the brick will be the best hard coloured brick and above that the best White Brick laid in the best Reach Lime". Also the brickwork "from the floor of the Tunnel [of the scoopwheel] shall be laid with Roman Cement, and any other part of the brickwork exposed to the action of the water or spray thereof laid in Roman Cement". Outside, the roof was covered with boards of wood to which the best Westmorland slates were pinned with copper nails and "well capped and pointed with neat lead ridges". The windows were glazed with "the best description of Window Glass", care being taken "that the panes fit easily into the iron frames to prevent their breaking by unequal expansion and contraction".

Inside, the cylinder, the pillars supporting the beam, and the bearing-block for the crank-shaft all rested on solid blocks of masonry built on the gravel bed. On top of the masonry, to take the weight of the engine itself, were laid strong slabs of Yorkshire pavers. The slab under the cylinder was to be 6 feet square and 18 inches thick, and there were others of a similar magnitude wherever weight or thrust had to be taken. "The whole of the aforesaid stones shall square up to the dimensions given and shall be laid solid and firmly bedded in their respective places without any filling or packing whatsoever." Through these pavers, and down through holes in the masonry, went long bolts to secure the cylinder, pillars and crankshaft plummer-block. These bolts were fastened at their lower ends by iron plates and cotters, but were free to move a little in the holes to allow the parts to be lined up. Two bolts through the masonry secured a large iron plate to which the crankshaft plummer-block was bolted by two more bolts and packed with wood allowing for final accurate adjustment. The cylinder was secured with four bolts direct to its paver, and the pillars with one each. The base of the pillar was cast integral with its shaft, so a slot was left at the bottom through which the nut on the end of the securing bolt could be tightened. The capital was separate and was secured by a cotter. These pillars took the weight and up-thrust of the beam which was mounted on two plummer-blocks.

Old "Waggon"-type boiler retained in the roof of the boiler-house at Timberland as a storage tank for water (R.H.C.)

Later type of Lancashire boiler at Pode Hole (1962), now used to store diesel oil (E.J.A.K.)

Front of Pinchbeck Spalding Marsh boiler, renewed in 1893 (E.J.A.K.)

The original boilers were the early type which had external fires below them. They were set in brickwork and the part of the work round the fireplaces was lined "with the best Stourbridge Bricks and Fire clay". Underneath, there was built a "good brick Sough to carry off the water when the boilers are emptied with a cast iron grate in each ashpit". The builder also had to fix "the Fire Doors, Grates, Bearers, Plates and Dampers which will be provided", to whitewash the walls of the engine- and boiler-houses and to clean and scour the floors with sand. Finally, he had to provide "a neat tablet of Ketton Stone for the front of the building and cut an inscription thereon as the Commissioners think fit".

At the Stretham engine, there were originally only two boilers, for a third was added later. The Hundred Foot engine had two when built, but the earlier engines had only one, with the possible exception of the Swaffham and Bottisham engine where Rennie made allowance in the plans for two although only one may have been installed. At Deeping Fen there was certainly only one for each engine, for in 1831 the Engineer stated "that it was necessary and desirable in case of accident that the boiler of one engine should be made

111

applicable to the service of the other which he showed (by a drawing) could be done by means of two curved pipes".[4] March West and Pinchbeck had only one boiler, although renewed, during their entire working life, and the first Ten Mile Bank engine had only one.[5] It was later discovered that it was more economical to fire two smaller boilers a little below their full capacity rather than work a larger one at its limit. Then came the stage when it was

generally understood to be the better way for a 40-horse engine to have three boilers of 30-horse power each, two to be at work, and one ready for cleansing or repairs if out of order. Experience has proved that two boilers of 30-horse power will generate steam for a 40-horse engine with *less fuel* than one 40-horse boiler, as the furnace does not want so often disturbing to replenish the fire (thereby letting in the cold air), and the combustion is more complete.[6]

At the beginning of the nineteenth century there were only three practicable types of water-raising machine if we exclude Savery's engine which was never really successful. The earliest form of pump which was used with the steam-engine was the lift-pump, but this was more suitable for raising a little water a long way rather than a large quantity of water a little way. Under normal conditions the water did not have to be raised more than 4 or 5 feet, although this would be considerably increased in times of flood. Although there were one or two places where the lift might be as great as 20 feet, the low height to which the water had to be raised prevented much use of atmospheric pressure with these pumps when used for land drainage. In addition, the water which had to be raised was full of mud and weeds which choked the valves and stopped the pumps working. The cost of erection was cheaper than a scoopwheel, but they were never popular in England, although, besides the one at Waldersea, one or two were erected on the Trent. "They were expensive and troublesome, and liable to get out of repair, and besides this, they would not perform half the amount of work that the wheels will",[7] but many were erected in Holland, notably the three stations which pumped the Harlemmermeer dry in 1852.

Another type of water-engine that was available at this time was the Archimedes' screw. One of these, worked by a windmill, was tried in 1741 to drain Deeping Fen, but it was soon abandoned.[8] The screw was never popular in England because, although it did not easily go wrong or become choked, the height which it lifted the water was difficult to vary. Since most of the windmills, and after them the steam-engines, pumped into rivers, it would have been necessary to make the screw long enough to reach above the floods, and this would have been very wasteful under normal conditions. Many were built in Holland where there was not the same liability to flooding. Two were installed in 1837 to drain the Zuidplas area, driven by 30 h.p. steam-engines, and this type of pump is again popular today for three modern ones have replaced the Mastenbroek steam-engine and scoop-wheels which ran from 1856 to 1962. These screws are driven by electric motors and have a special sluice which can be lowered to vary the height of the lift.

The only other choice available to these early engineers was the scoopwheel. A scoop-wheel is like an undershot waterwheel turned round in the opposite direction, so that instead of being rotated by the water flowing through the race from the mill-pond, it pushes the water up the race from the drain behind to the river in front.[9] The earliest wheels, worked by windmills or horses, were made of wood, but the Ten Mile Bank engine and the Swaffham and Bottisham engine and all the later ones had wheels made of cast iron. On smaller engines such as the March West and Pinchbeck, there might be only a single set of spokes, and the whole wheel formed of only two castings. On the bigger engines there would be two sets of spokes which were cast separately, besides other castings for the segments of the circumference. Round the edge of the ironwork there were cast sockets

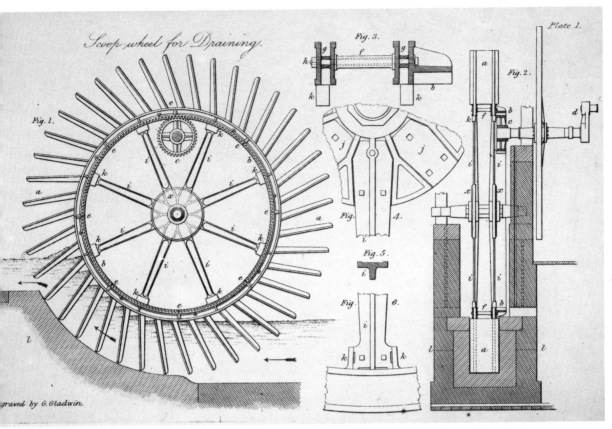

Drawing of a scoopwheel, J. Glynn, Soc. of Arts, *vol. 51, 1838*

into which start-posts were driven and secured by pegs of iron or oak. There were usually two of these starts, made from oak, to which were nailed boards of fir to form the ladles or scoops which raised the water.

The ladles rotated in a track or trough of hewn stone or masonry shaped to fit them. This had to be close fitting to prevent the water running back round the edges. Even so, the clearance or space between the wheel and the sides and bottom varied from $\frac{4}{10}$ inch in the best machines to $\frac{3}{4}$ inch and even more in others.[10] It is difficult to say how much leakage this gap allowed, because it was counteracted by the impetus imparted to the water by the rotation of the wheel. This speed varied from engine to engine, the average being about 8 feet per second at the circumference.[11] Joseph Glynn

found about six feet per second to be the best speed for the circumference of the wheel, as that velocity gives sufficient centrifugal force to hold the water up against the "breast" of the wheel-track or trough of masonry, and yet not so much as to cause its being carried up by the float-boards past the point of delivery.[12]

The centrifugal force helped to throw the water off the ladles, but a certain amount of water and spray was carried round with the wheel. If the wheel turned too rapidly, water was lifted much higher than necessary and flung all over the place. It is a very fine sight to see a windmill working a scoopwheel in a strong wind, for the wheel almost disappears in a cloud of spray as the ladles fling the water into the air where it is whipped away by the wind. But this all represents wasted energy, which with the steam-engine meant a waste of money in the form of fuel.

Flood door and outlet sluice of the scoop-wheel at Middleton (R.H.C.)

It will be realized that a scoopwheel could not raise water even half its diameter, or the water would run back over the tops of the ladles into the fen. To help prevent this, and also to get rid of the water more quickly, the ladles were inclined downwards at the point where they discharged the water. The problem was how to compromise between an angle that would effectively pick up the water in the drain and yet allow it to run off freely into the river. The ladles were made to tilt down "from the radial line at an angle varying from 25 to 55, but generally about 40 degrees. . . . The best results are probably obtained from wheels having an angle of ingress of 30 and of egress of 45 when the water is at its mean level."[13] So far as is known, "feathering" the ladles was never tried, but various experiments were adopted to try and overcome this problem, although in this early period little was done to improve efficiency. At first there was nothing to control the supply of water to

114

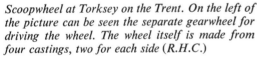

Scoopwheel at Torksey on the Trent. On the left of the picture can be seen the separate gearwheel for driving the wheel. The wheel itself is made from four castings, two for each side (R.H.C.)

Internal gearing driving a scoopwheel, Thurlton engine. The gear teeth are cast on the inside rim of the scoopwheel (R.H.C.)

the wheel, and nothing to ease the flow of water into the river. All that was done was to fit one or two doors like lock-gates to stop the water from the river running back into the fen when the engine was not working.

The scoopwheels rotated at about 4 r.p.m., while the steam-engines made between 12 and 20 r.p.m., so some form of gearing was necessary between the wheel and the engine. At first an ordinary form of gear was used. One gear-wheel, keyed on to the end of the engine crankshaft, drove another larger gear-wheel which was keyed on to the axle of the scoop-wheel. This system was employed on the engines built in Deeping Fen where "the cast iron toothed wheels were of necessity very strong, more so than any I had seen, being 15 ins. across the face of the wheel and the pitch of the teeth 5 ins.".[14] Not only the toothed wheels had to be made very strong, but also the spokes to transmit the driving forces to the ladles, with the result that the wheels were exceedingly heavy. The way to lighten them seems to have been discovered by accident. The next large engine to be built after the two for Deeping Fen was the Hundred Foot engine which pumped into a tidal river. The designer, Joseph Glynn, fitted two gears so the wheel could be turned faster at low tide. There was a sliding pinion which engaged with an ordinary gear for the fast speed, but which could be meshed with a wheel having "internal teeth"[15] for a slower speed. In this form of epicyclic gear, the driving forces were transmitted at the circumference of the wheel directly to the

The scoopwheel of the Worlingham engine; note the internal gearing on the main rim (R.H.C.)

ladles. Consequently, the spokes could be made much lighter, in some cases becoming only tension rods. All the later engines of any size had this epicyclic-gear arrangement.

Even so, the weight of the wheels remained enormous, often being "as much or more than the total body of water lifted at each revolution. The larger wheels, of say 30 feet in diameter, weigh from 30 to 40 tons, and therefore require very heavy foundations and expensive masonry work for the wheel race."[16] The first wheel at the Hundred Foot engine weighed 54 tons,[17] and the later one, which was the largest in the Fens, with a diameter of 50 feet, weighed 75 tons. This wheel turned at 3 r.p.m. and discharged 213 tons per minute.[18] The wheels were mounted on large plain bearings which rested on the masonry of the wheel-trough. Although such bearings caused more friction, they were necessary to prevent excessive wear. If the bearings wore quickly or unevenly, the ladle-boards would scrape against the sides of the trough. Likewise the foundations had to be very rigid and well built for the slightest settlement would cause the wheel to grind against the sides.

The English scoopwheels were much greater in diameter than those built in Holland. There a larger volume of water had to be lifted a smaller height, so it was quite common to see two or three wheels driven by the same engine working side by side. At Spaarndam two sets of five wheels side by side are still worked by diesel-engines, but except for the Ten Mile Bank engine, there was never more than a single wheel to each engine in England (at Haddenham, there was added later a second much smaller wheel to lift the water up to the first as the drain had sunk so low, but this was the "double-lift" system and not side by side).

116

Dutch engine with scoopwheels on either side

Conditions in the Fens varied so much from year to year that it is difficult to estimate how much water had to be pumped out by these wheels. With windmills, there could be no guaranteed drainage, so during the winter they were worked as often as the wind permitted, but during the summer they were "set down" as soon as the land was dry and they remained out of use until the following winter unless there was an emergency. There could be no scientific application of such a power, but the advent of the steam-engine meant that the water-level could be controlled and this altered the type of agriculture that could be pursued.

Ideally, the water-level should be kept at a predetermined level, usually at a mark on the engine-house, but in practice that is impossible to maintain unless there are pumps powerful enough to pump out the rain as it falls. The average rainfall could be computed with adequate accuracy, but the engines had to be able to cope with any reasonable emergency. At the Stretham engine, the greatest amount that fell in one day was 3·70 inches (26 August 1912), while over an inch was quite common in a single day. A rainfall of 19·95 inches, a little below the annual average for the whole year, is "equal to 2,014 tons of water that has fallen on one acre of land. Taking the taxable land at 5,000 acres, it is equal to 10,070,000 tons."[19] The average fall of rain and rate of evaporation have been discussed earlier, and it will be clear that, because so much more water is evaporated in summer than in winter, it is safe to keep the water-level in the drains higher in summer. This has been a long-standing practice, partly to provide water for livestock since there are no springs in the Fens.[20]

117

Since the rainfall is not regular throughout the year, the amount that has to be pumped out depends on the state of the land and the comparative wetness of the seasons.

When the land is dry and the soke low, a good deal of what falls is absorbed by the Land and little is to be carried away by the Drains, but when the soak is high, and much rain falls, the most of it is to be carried off. . . . The soak may be in general kept low as well as the water in the drains – a considerable quantity of the water that falls when the Drains and Lands are in this state will be retained by the land, and the Drains will act as Reservoirs – so that time will be given for the engines to carry it off before the land can be injured – on this account the Engines may be made of a smaller size than would otherwise be necessary.[21]

Much depended on the season, whether there were periods of continual rain or whether there were scattered showers between which the water had a chance to evaporate.

If the rains fall frequently, the Engine will be required to work at frequent intervals and as a certain portion of fuel will be consumed at each interval in setting the engine to work and letting down the fires, this fuel may be said to be consumed without any useful effect, whereas when rain continues for a considerable period together, the engine being once set to work, all the fuel afterwards consumed till the water is taken out is effectively employed.[22]

This shows what great skill and judgement was needed to work these engines economically. Every time the Stretham engine had to be started from cold, it required over $\frac{1}{2}$ ton of coal to warm it up before it could begin to work. In winter it was usually the practice to keep a small fire in one boiler so the engine could be started quickly in times of emergency. To guard further against any catastrophe, Rennie recommended keeping the water in the drains low so that they could act as reservoirs.

To work such an Engine to advantage, it would be judicious to keep the water low in the Drains at . . . the beginning of November, and the breaking up of the Frosts, by this means the drains would be prepared to receive the water which fell and give the Engine time to work it out before it could do any injury to the land and thereby render overfiring unnecessary – in the summer, the engine would seldom require to be worked, and indeed at several other periods of the year.[23]

This method of working led Rennie to recommend a smaller size of engine than later experience showed was necessary. The figures he gives for the Upware engine in the Swaffham and Bottisham District and for the Deeping Fen engines show that he allowed 10 h.p. for every 2,500 acres. Joseph Glynn assumed that it was only the rain that had to be pumped out, and made no allowance for upland waters or seepage. He took the average rainfall as 26 inches per annum, and supposed that in any one month there might fall

3 inches depth of rain, of which one inch is absorbed and evaporated . . . [leaving] 1¼ cubic feet to every square yard of land, . . . and this gives 7260 cubic feet of water to the acre. . . .
   Suppose, therefore, we wish to drain 1000 acres of fen or marsh-land, and that the upland waters were all banked out; we have an excess of rain equal to 7,260,000 cubic feet of water to raise and get rid of. A good steam engine of 10 horses power will do this in 232 hours, or less than 20 days, working 12 hours per day, and I have found these calculations fully supported in practise.[24]

These calculations show that Glynn allowed 10 h.p. to every 1,000 acres that would be drained. It is not possible to give any ideal figure, because it depends on how long the farmers are prepared to tolerate a certain amount of excess water in the drains. The

118

following tables show the gradual increase in horse-power, an increase that cannot be accounted for solely by the additional lift as the fens shrank.

Originally drained by seventy-five windmills.

Ten Mile Bank Station
1820   30 h.p. steam-engine.
1842   Replaced by 80 h.p. steam-engine.
1880   Power of this engine increased by new valves and higher boiler pressure.
1912   Twin steam-engines (each 250 h.p.) replaced the scoopwheel.
1935   340 h.p. Allen oil-engine.
1947   360 h.p. Allen oil-engine. 1935 and 1947 installations form a twin set.

Hundred Foot Station
1830   80 h.p. steam-engine.
1882   Power increased to about 224 h.p. by improved valve gear and increased boiler pressure.
1914   400 h.p. Gwynnes steam-engine and pump replaced scoopwheel, discharge 200 tons a minute.
1926   230 h.p. Mirrlees oil-engine in a separate house in addition to Gwynnes set.
1951   540 h.p. Ruston oil-engine replaced Gwynnes set. 1926 and 1951 installations form a twin set.

WATERBEACH LEVEL
Originally drained by three windmills, one more added in 1814.

Stretham Engine
1831   60 h.p.
1888   Increased to 90 h.p. by higher boiler pressure.
1909   Horse-power increased by new valves.
1925   240 h.p. Mirrlees diesel-engine added close by, but steam-engine used in emergency till 1940.

Cam Bank Engines
1947   Two 135 h.p. Allen diesel-engines, Mirrlees retained as stand-by engine.

The smaller the horse-power of the steam-engine, the longer it would take to pump out the water, but it has not been possible to determine what was the most economical size, partly because farmers came to demand a more efficient standard of drainage which necessitated more powerful machinery. Rennie would seem to have underestimated the power required to do the work in a reasonable time, but he was a pioneer in this field whereas Glynn was able to benefit from earlier engines which had been erected. Yet in all these districts where steam-engines were first erected, at least some of the windmills were retained as long as they would continue to work.

In very few cases can the whole cost of a complete pumping station be determined. The figures given below are an attempt to see the basic cost without taking into account any additional expenses for Acts of Parliament or work on the drains. The picture is complicated because various contractors would supply different parts, and it is not always possible to identify them in the Account Books. For example, the Littleport and Downham Commissioners paid £1,800 for the machinery of their Ten Mile Bank engine,[25] exclusive of buildings and perhaps of scoopwheels. The total they expected to pay may have been nearer £6,000, for having already paid £900 towards their engine, they decided to try and borrow £5,000 on the security of the taxes.[26] This compares with £6,300 which Rennie estimated for the Swaffham and Bottisham engine, and since neither of these engines was

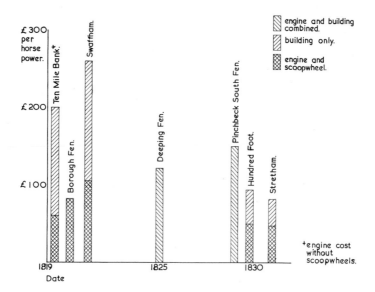

Cost of Steam-engines

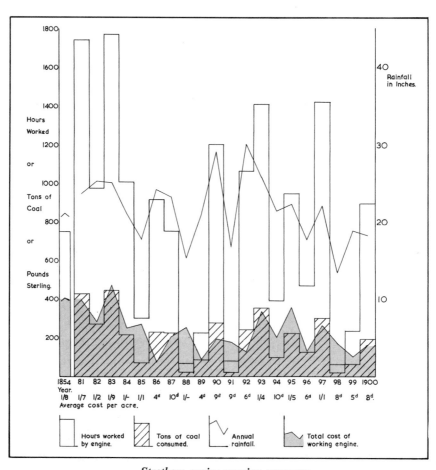

Stretham engine running expenses

over 30 h.p., the cost worked out between £200 and £260 for each horse-power of the engine. In 1825 Deeping Fen paid about £17,000 for two engines totalling 140 h.p.,[27] and in 1830 the Hundred Foot engine of the Littleport and Downham Commissioners cost about £7,500 for 80 h.p.[28] In the following year, the 60 h.p. Stretham engine cost only £4,950, and Joseph Glynn found that

the first cost of the work varies in almost every district, from the nature of the substrata; but I generally have found that it amounted to about 20s. an acre for the requisite machinery and buildings: that is to say, an engine of 40 horses' power, with its scoopwheel, machinery and buildings, erected for the drainage of 4000 acres of land, cost about 4000 l. I have found this to be the case in four different districts.[29]

This shows that by 1830 the cost of these engines had been reduced to under £100 per horse-power, or under half that of the first engines in the Fens. For engines that were not rotative but worked a pump, there was a similar fall in cost. Rennie had estimated £5,750 for a steam-engine and pump of about 50 h.p. for the Waterbeach Level in 1814,[30] although this was never built, and in 1832 Waldersea District paid only £3,000 for a 60 h.p. engine and pump.[31]

Technical improvements in the steam-engine helped to reduce their running costs, as did experience gained with their use. One reason why the Deeping Fen engines did not have a greater influence and create an example for others to follow may have been due to the inadequacy of the drains. In January 1828, "the Superintendent represented and the Trustees concurred in the opinion that the main drains are very insufficient for the drainage of the fens and that in consequence the Engines have not been rendered effectual to the extent of their power and a considerable waste of fuel has been occasioned".[32] The experiments conducted nearly two years later reveal much interesting information about the performance of these engines and the factors that had to be taken into consideration in their design. The first trials took place in October 1829.

It having been understood at the last meeting of the Trustees that if the weather continued fine so as to admit of the water in the drains remaining without increase for several days that both engines should be started at a given hour on a day of which notice was to be given to the Trustees and that stakes should be placed in the South Drove Drain at a mile distant from each other, the

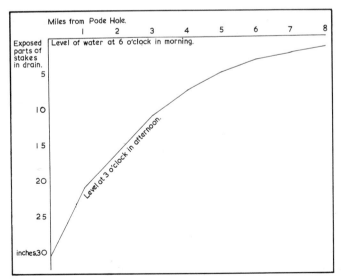

Test at Pode Hole,
15 October 1829

121

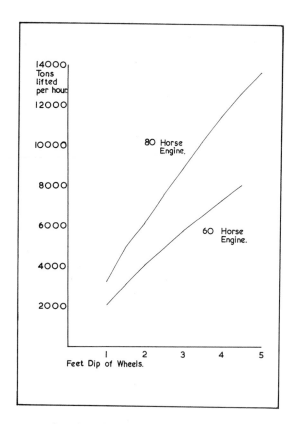

Discharge of water by the engines at Pode Hole, October 1829

tops of such stakes being on a level with the surface of the water so that the effect of the engines in reducing the water in such drains might be practically ascertained, and Thursday the 15th. of October having been fixed for the purpose, and notice of the day having been given to the Trustees by Mr. Simson the Superintendent.

Both engines were started at 6 o'clock in the morning with a four feet dip and after being kept constantly at work until three o'clock in the afternoon, the water was found to have been lowered at the Engine thirty inches and a half – at the first mile, 21 inches – at the second mile, 16 inches ... and at the eighth mile, one inch and a half. There was a fall at the Bridge over the Turnpike road of one inch, to this extent the bridge forms an impediment to the drainage, the curve in the drain about a mile and three quarters south of such bridge was also found to occasion considerable obstruction to the passage of water to the engines. . . .

The Superintendent and Engineer . . . explaining and proving the advantage that would result from an enlargement of the drains and that if the same were enlarged to the extent proposed by the Superintendent's report . . . the discharge of water by the engines would be increased by 40 per cent and a saving be effected of 25 per cent in the coals.[33]

Figures were also given of the water discharged by the wheels, which show how much more water was pumped out when the wheels had a deeper dip. If the drains near the engines could be kept fuller, fewer revolutions of the wheels would be needed with consequent saving in costs and time. At the suggestion of Lord Carrington, one of the Trustees, Mylne came to Deeping Fen after he had visited the Upware and Hundred Foot engines.[34] His recommendations for the enlargement of the drains were carried out over the next two years at a cost of over £7,000. One result was that the remaining private windmills on the farms in the district were removed and the entire drainage done by the steam-engines, and there would also have been a saving in the amount of fuel used because the water could

122

reach the engines more quickly. It required a certain amount of power to rotate the scoop-wheels and overcome friction, even when there was no water to be pumped. Since this was a constant quantity, it was relatively less when most water was being raised.[35] The following table shows that the fuel consumption could not be reduced below a certain minimum, however little water there was in the drains.

EXPERIMENT MADE WITH THE EIGHTY HORSE ENGINE AT PODE HOLE ON THE 18TH DAY OF JULY 1830

Time the Engine was at work.	Coal burnt, bushels.	Mean lift at which the Eng. worked.	Main dip of the wheel.	Weight of water raised per hour.
		ft. ins.	ft. ins.	Tons.
1st. hours trial	12$\frac{1}{2}$	6 7$\frac{1}{2}$	3 4	9,840
2 ,, ,,	12	6 10	2 10	8,520
3 ,, ,,	11$\frac{1}{2}$	7 2	2 6	7,560
4 ,, ,,	11	7 5	2 2	6,660
5 ,, ,,	10	7 6	1 10	5,700
6 ,, ,,	10	7 6	1 6	4,740
7 ,, ,,	10	7 6	1 3	4,220
8 ,, ,,	10	7 6	1 2	3,990

The fuel used during this trial, was Yorkshire coal, of which the average consumption was about 10$\frac{1}{2}$ lbs. per horse-power per hour. From 8 to 9 lbs. of Newcastle coal would, with this engine, be found to do the same quantity of work.[36]

Rennie expected the Upware engine to burn 14 lbs. of coal per hour,[37] and the Deeping Fen engines around 12 lbs.[38]

The only definite figures to show the cost of running these engines at this time come from Deeping Fen. For other districts it has not been possible to isolate any accurate figures from the Account Books. The figures show that Rennie's estimate of £1,500 per annum proved to be a little too low, but the rainfall was greater than he had allowed.

RUNNING COSTS OF ENGINES IN DEEPING FEN YEAR ENDING 9 APRIL 1828

	£	s.	d.
909 chaldrons of Yorkshire coals, averaging 27s. 1d. per chaldron when delivered at Pode Hole	1,231	13	3
Tallow, oil and candles	157	16	3
Hemp, etc., for packing	12	12	6
Engineer's salary	200	0	0
To which ought to be added for contingencies in repair	100	0	0
	£1,702	2	0

8 April 1829. Rainfall (probably January to January) 30·25 inches.

	£	s.	d.
1,240 chaldrons of coals, averaging 25s. 6d. when delivered	1,581	0	0
Tallow, oil and candles	135	0	0
Hemp, etc., for packing	30	0	0
Engineer's and Superintendent's salaries	265	0	0
Repairs of engines	217	0	0
	£2,081	0	0

For 1830. Rainfall 34·38 inches. "Glen Bank broke."

840 chaldrons of coals, averaging 23s. when delivered	975	0	0
Tallow, oil and candles	60	0	0
Hemp for packing	18	0	0
Engineer's and Superintendent's salaries	265	0	0
Repairs of engines	217	0	0
	£1,535	0	0

For 1831. Rainfall 34·32 inches. "Glen Bank broke."

1,400 tons of coals, 15s.	1,050	0	0
Tallow, oil, candles, packing materials	120	0	0
Engineer's salary	200	0	0
Repairs of engines	300	0	0
	£1,670	0	0

For 1832. Rainfall 28·87 inches.

Coals, tallow, Engineer's salary and repairs	£2,054	0	0

The rainfall figures are taken from a document found among the Stretham Engine Records, the other figures from the Deeping Fen Accounts.

If these figures are reduced to find out the cost per acre, then taking Deeping Fen at 30,000 acres,[39] for £1,500, the expenses will be 1s. per acre per annum and £2,000 will be 1s. 4d., to which ought to be added 8d. for five per cent interest on £20,000. For Sutton St Edmund, an annual expense of £200 spread over 4,000 acres works out at 1s. per acre, and £320 for the Borough Fen engine is just over 1s.[40] In 1814 Rennie thought that the cost for the engine he was recommending for the Waterbeach Level was not likely "to exceed £700 per annum, which is not quite 3/8 per acre".[41] He was writing at a time of high prices due to war, and when it has been possible to work out accurate figures for the Stretham engine, the costs were much reduced. The years between 1881 and 1900 had a rainfall above the average, and towards the end of that period wages, which had remained remarkably steady since 1830, began to rise. These trends would be offset to a certain extent by the installation of new boilers which were more economical, so the figures may be fairly representative. Over the period of twenty years, the running costs of the engine work out at 11d. per acre per annum, to which ought to be added 3d. for the Superintendent's salary. Also for the early years 1s. must be added for the interest on the mortgage which was finally paid off in 1878. These figures bear out a statement by Glynn:

The engines work about four months out of the twelve, at intervals varying of course with the season. Where the districts are tolerably large, and the drainage effected by steam power, the annual expenses including all charges, will not exceed 2/6 an acre.[42]

It was reckoned that when the mortgage had been discharged, all the expenses for the Waldersea District, including the steam-engine, would be covered by a tax of 1s. 6d. an acre.[43]

How did this compare with windmills? Very few figures to show how much it cost to work a windmill have been found. In 1709 Bateson was advocating drainage by a natural channel and not windmills, so his figures are probably biased. He reckoned "both these engines for Tidd and Newton low-lands, being 2150 Acres, or there abouts, will cost one Year with another, one Shilling an Acre, which is 107 £ 10 s. a year".[44] The Haddenham Level Account Books show that they were spending a much lower figure on their five mills for repairs and attendance.

Year starting in Michaelmas	Attendance			Repairs			Per Acre (Roughly)
	£	s.	d.	£	s.	d.	d.
1739–40	37	6	5	43	15	$7\frac{1}{2}$	3
40–41	33	19	7	39	3	$5\frac{1}{2}$	$2\frac{3}{4}$
43–44	22	7	6	5	11	$\frac{1}{2}$	1
44–45	84	1	6	39	1	2	$4\frac{3}{4}$

The only other figures are those given by Wing when he was trying to obtain estimates to show the savings that would be made if the North Level Main Drain were dug. The answers he received from various friends stated that the costs of windmill drainage varied from £150 to about £5 for working and repairing each mill every year. He therefore averaged these figures to £80 per annum for a large mill and £25 for a small one.[45] If it is taken that "a fen windmill for draining costs about £1,000 and is supposed sufficient for 1,000 acres",[46] then the average costs per acre for a large mill are 1s. 6d. Using the same figures for the four windmills of the Waterbeach Level, which are known to have been large mills, the average is 1s. 4d. per acre per annum. This indicates that the steam-engines were slightly cheaper to work, and this agrees with a perusal of the Waterbeach Level Account Books. It has not been possible to show any figures from these, but by deducting those expenses that can be definitely ascertained, and assuming the rest was spent on the drains and the engines, then the cost was a little less under steam than wind power. The capital investment in windmills had been spread over a number of years so that the cost did not seem so much and it was difficult at first to find the large sum to finance the building of a steam-engine. Once the steam-engine was established, the cost was not much different from using windmills, and there was the certainty that the Fens would be properly drained at the right time.

NOTES

1. J. Rennie, Letter Books, vol. 11, p. 103, 28 March 1820.
2. J. Glynn, "Draining Land by Steam Power", *Trans. Soc. of Arts*, vol. 51 (1838), p. 18.
3. The quotations following are taken from the Articles of Agreement between Charles Briggs and the Waterbeach Level Commissioners for building the Stretham engine.
4. Deeping Fen Minutes, 14 February 1831.
5. Littleport and Downham District Order Book, 24 April 1833.
6. J. A. Clarke, "The Great Level of the Fens", *J.R.A.S.*, vol. 8 (1847), p. 98.
7. J. A. Clarke, "On the Farming of Lincolnshire", *J.R.A.S.*, vol. 12 (1851), p. 324.
8. W. H. Wheeler, *The History of the Fens of South Lincolnshire* (2nd ed. 1897), p. 323.
9. L. Gibbs, "Pumping Machinery in the Fenland and by the Trent-side", *Min. Proc. Inst. Civ. Eng.*, vol. XCIV (1888), p. 267.
10. W. H. Wheeler, *The Drainage of Fens . . .* (1888), p. 74.
11. L. Gibbs, op. cit., p. 268.
12. J. Glynn, op. cit., p. 15.
13. W. H. Wheeler, *The Drainage of Fens . . .* (1888), pp. 74, 76.
14. J. Glynn, op. cit., p. 15.
15. ibid., p. 16.
16. W. H. Wheeler, *The Drainage of Fens . . .* (1888), p. 71.

17. J. Glynn, op. cit., p. 15.
18. W. H. Wheeler, *The Drainage of Fens* . . . (1888), pp. 71, 83, 107.
19. Waterbeach Level Engine Log Book, May 1846.
20. ibid., 28 May 1889.
    Commissioners Meeting, Stretham, Starting Mark to be 4′ 9″ from May 1 to Sep. 1, and 4′ 6″ other parts of the year.
21. J. Rennie, Letter Books, vol. 11, pp. 341–2, 6 December 1820.
22. ibid., p. 122, 13 April 1820.
23. ibid., p. 123, 13 April 1820.
24. J. Glynn, op. cit., pp. 10–11.
25. Littleport and Downham Order Book, 1 July 1818.
26. ibid., 26 April 1820, and Account Book, 7 March 1820.
27. Deeping Fen Accounts, 7 April 1825.
28. Littleport and Downham Account Book, June 1829–April 1830.
29. J. Glynn, op. cit., p. 13.
30. J. Rennie, Letter Books, vol. 8, p. 22, 5 March 1814.
31. S. Jonas, "On the Farming of Cambridgeshire", *J.R.A.S.*, vol. 7 (1846), p. 64.
32. Deeping Fen Minutes, 26 January 1828.
33. ibid., 30 December 1829.
34. ibid., 15 May 1830.
35. G. Cuppari, "On the Practical Results obtained from various Water-raising Machines in Holland", *Trans. Inst. Civ. Eng.*, vol. 75 (1883–4), p. 264.
36. J. Glynn, op. cit., p. 12.
    The waterwheel is 28 feet in diameter, its float-boards are $5\frac{1}{2}$ feet in depth by 5 feet wide, and they travel with a mean velocity of 6 feet in a second. The section of the stream delivered, when the engine has its full dip, is, therefore, $27\frac{1}{2}$ square feet, and the quantity discharged is 165 cubic feet, equal to more than $4\frac{1}{2}$ tons of water in one second, or about 16,200 tons in one hour.
37. J. Rennie, Letter Books, vol. 11, p. 123, 28 March 1820.
    When the Engine is at work exerting her full power, the quantity of good Newcastle Coals she will consume will be about one Cwt. and a half p. hour and consequently in twenty four hours 36 cwt., but as this will seldom be the case, the quantity consumed will be proportionally less and this will depend on the state of the Ouse and the water in the Fen – If the water is high in the Ouse but of a moderate height in the Fen, the more power will be required and vice versa, perhaps if I was to state the quantity at one chaldron p. day of 27 cwt. (the weight of a London Chaldron) I should not be much wide of the truth.
38. ibid., p. 343, 6 December 1820.
39. ibid., p. 342, 6 December 1820.
40. T. Wing, *Considerations of the Principles of Mr. Rennie's Plans for the Drainage of the North Level* . . (1820), p. 22.
41. J. Rennie, Letter Books, vol. 8, p. 24, 5 March 1814.
42. J. Glynn, op. cit., p. 13.
43. S. Jonas, op. cit., p. 64.
44. P. Bateson, *An Answer to some Objections* . . . (1710), p. 13.
45. T. Wing, Letter Books, 1 February 1820.
46. W. Gooch, *Cambridge* (1813), p. 240.

CHAPTER IX

A Wheat-growing Country

A GREAT DISCOVERY

By 1830 the main difficulties connected with the steam-engine had been overcome and the people in the Fens at last had a dependable method of drainage. The former conditions began to be forgotten, and even laughed at, and one person reflecting on earlier visits to the Fens wrote:

In 1807, I paid my first visit to the fens around Downham and Southery, and par consequence, my first exploits with a jumping pole. I reckoned this the best part of farming. It was capital fun, for the drains were wide and full enough to afford plenty of sport in clearing them. Up to that time, but little had been done towards drainage, except when it might please heaven to send wind to propel the mills: a lay of wind was sure to keep all the district under water, or at any rate to keep it sufficiently wet to put a stop to all cultivation.[1]

By the middle of the century, people could look back and see the vast changes that had taken place through the improvement in drainage. The former picture most farmers had was of their land being under water during the winter months. If the spring was dry and there was enough wind to drive the mills, they would manage to sow oats by the end of April, although the greater part was not sown before the middle or later end of May. Compared with later improvements, the general aspect of the country at that time was wretched indeed, with bad roads, miserable houses and farm-buildings, and for much of the time water covering the land.[2] But through the scouring and deepening of the rivers and outfalls, and through the introduction of the steam-engine, "the drainage has become so complete, that the land is now esteemed almost *certain* from being injured by floods".[3]

The steam-engine was at last able to guarantee that the soak or acid water in the peat would be kept down to a level which would not injure the growing crops. Rennie had recommended keeping the water at least 2 feet under the surface of the land,[4] but Glynn had adopted a standard of 18 inches.[5] The shrinkage of the peat through the better drainage made either of these difficult to maintain, but the lower depth was better for the farmer. This was well demonstrated in Deeping Fen where the peat had shrunk about 2 feet by 1848 so that the engines did not keep the water in the drains during the winter lower than 15 inches from the surface. This meant that the soil was generally wet and lost a great deal of its goodness through the manure soaking into the drains.[6] By this time it was thought necessary to keep the water-level at least $2\frac{1}{2}$ or 3 feet below the surface,[7] and a modern fenman would aim to keep it more. One of the farmers in Deeping Fen erected his own engine on a low part of the land and kept the water on his own farm at least 2 feet lower than on those around. His crops were much better than his neighbours,[8] clearly demonstrating that the lower depth of water in the drains was an improvement for agriculture. The only way of remedying this was by lowering the scoopwheels of the engines.

When the water-level was properly under control, the drainage was often better than on some of the upland farms. While Jonas was touring through the Fens to write his report on farming in Cambridgeshire for the Royal Agricultural Society, he found the fen farmers ploughing and carting, but he had not been able to move a plough on his highland farm

127

The Holme Post. In 1852 this was driven into the peat until it was completely buried. The disappearance of the peat through subsequent drainage has uncovered most of the post, a shrinkage of about 12 feet

owing to the wet.[9] In summer, the advent of the steam-engine was equally advantageous, for since the Fens had no natural springs, water had to be let into the ditches through sluices to supply the cattle with drinking water. When there was a steam-engine, this could be done without fear that a sudden thunderstorm might flood the ditches and drown the standing crops.

On the other hand, the steam-engine hastened the shrinkage of the peat. It is obvious that Glynn had not realized the extent of this problem, or he would have been forced to make some provision for it in the design and construction of his steam-engines and scoopwheels. Both the Hundred Foot and the Stretham engines had to have their scoopwheels lowered within twenty years of their erection so they could drain deeper. It was the practice to start pumping when the water had risen to a mark on the engine-house and to continue pumping until another mark was uncovered. In this way the levels for controlling the pumping were not directly related to the land level. This meant that the peat shrank rapidly when a new drainage level had first been established, but the rate of shrinkage slowed down the nearer the water-level was approached. If the water-level in the drains had been kept a constant 2 feet below the top of the peat as it shrank, then the peat would have vanished more rapidly. As it was, the drainage would be improved for a period after the installation

128

of steam-engines, but there would follow a slow deterioration in conditions until the land became too water-logged. Then the drainage level had to be lowered and the whole process began all over again, but at last it was possible to be reasonably certain of the drainage so agriculture could be pursued with much greater confidence.

At first the old agricultural methods of pare and burn, then sow with cole seed and follow by oats or wheat, were continued even after steam-engines had been introduced. The wheat crop that was grown had an uncertain hold in the soil and produced a long weak straw, easily bent or broken, with an ear of small size.[10] But now that the water-level could be kept under control, a great transformation took place in the Fens on the peat land.

The consequence of this has been a new system of farming, and the general introduction of wheat crops, and the practise of *claying* or *marling the land*. This complete drainage has enabled the farmers to dig for these earths with success; and their benefit from their being laid on the land, is as great as that effected on the light sands of Norfolk and by the same means.[11]

Claying the land completely changed fen agriculture. The method of doing it varied slightly, but the account written by Samuel Jonas, himself a farmer but not in the Fens, gives a good picture of how the process appeared to an outsider.

CLAYING

This is done by opening furrows in the field intended to be clayed, about 14 yards apart, parallel to each other. The workman commences at one end by sinking a hole about 5 feet long, and about 4 feet wide: this hole is sunk perpendicularly; and when he arrives at the clay, which varies in depth from the surface from 2 to 7 or 10 feet, he throws out about 3 spit, which is about 3 feet deep, of this clay on each side of the hole, half the clay on one side and half on the other. The vegetable matter that is dug out of the first hole is spread on the surface of the land; he then proceeds to sink holes or pits all up the furrows, about one foot from each other, so that this space thus left acts as a wedge to prevent the sides of the drain from slipping in. In digging the second hole, the peat earth is thrown into the first hole, and thus the moor or *bear's muck* dug out of each hole is made to fill up the preceeding one. The tools used for this work are – a small light shovel or spoon, with very thin sharp cutting edges, and about 12 to 14 inches deep – a light wooden shovel, made as a scoop for throwing out the water as it runs into the hole from the sides of the vegetable matter – and a bill or axe. And each man has on a pair of large fen boots, which are made water-tight. Before the workman commences operations, he drives a strong stake deep into the end of the drain, onto which a strong rope is fastened, with a noose tied full of knots; this hangs down the hole and by it. When he has finished by throwing out the quantity of clay required, he pulls himself up out of the pit. But sometimes the men are required to do so before the work is finished, in consequence of the drains slipping in upon them. The bill is in constant requisition to cut and clear out the stumps and roots of trees, which are found just upon the fen clay, thus evidently proving that this clay was the original surface of the soil, and that the vegetable matter had grown up and risen above them.[12]

The great improvement that resulted from mixing clay with peat soils had been known for a long time, although it was probably first discovered by accident. It was noticed that where clay had been dug out of the bottom of deep drains and mixed with the peat, there the grass grew better and grain crops were heavier and did not so easily fall to the ground.[13] The clay lay at varying depths below the greater part of the Fens, in places quite close to the surface and easily accessible. It was known that claying or marling could double the value of the land[14] because it gave weight and substance to the peat and also neutralized the acid.[15] Arthur Young realized that the expense of carting it on to the land would probably be too great so he recommended that it would be much cheaper to sink circular cassoons through the bog to the sound soil beneath, and, what ever it may be, to dig it, wind it up as chalk is raised for manure in Hertfordshire, and wheel it onto the surface in barrows, as the same people do with that manure. I do not know that this has ever been tried, but would answer.[16]

It was about a generation later that Young's suggestions began to be carried out.[17] Wells remarked in 1830 that "An entirely new plan of management is now becoming very general, namely, what is termed 'claying the land'. This mode of management is so very modern, that the author finds some difficulty in giving an accurate description of its singular process."[18] It may be wondered why this system had not been applied long before if it really gave such spectacular results. The danger was that if the clayed land became wet and were flooded, it was often less productive than the peat without clay.[19] Unless the level of water in the fen could be properly controlled, it was not worth while risking the capital needed to be spent in claying if the soil might become worse through this process.

The type of soil under the peat varied from area to area, but the greater part was beds of either Kimmeridge or Oxford Clay. Different clay had a different effect, the best for the purpose being

of the most solid glutinous kind, so that when it is dug, as much, according to the farmers expression, should come up on the back as on the front of the spade. However wet the place from which it is taken, it should feel solid when rolled in the hand: if it be loose and liquid, it probably contains too much fine sand; if gritty, coarse sand. When tried in water, according to Mr. Rham's process, it should not fall to pieces, but dissolve with great difficulty, and should afterward remain suspended in the water, not letting fall much sediment of sand; when dry it should be hard, compact, and rather smooth. If it throws up air-bubbles on being mixed with an acid, I should like it the better.[20]

The extraction of the clay was often attended with difficulty and danger, especially if it lay a long way below the surface. Although a bulwark was left between the pits to act as a buttress and sometimes wooden boards were used to support the sides, the sides were liable to cave in and there was always a risk of men being buried.[21] In some areas, no suitable soil lay beneath the surface so that clay had to be carted on to it from elsewhere. Littleport Fen was like this in places, for the subsoil was sand which could give no strength to the peat. Some clay was carted on to it from adjoining lands with great success, but where the cost was too great to do this, the land still remained in a wild state, growing very weak crops.[22]

The limiting factor in the application of clay was of course cost. Where clay lay close to the surface, more loads could be raised from each of the holes, so that the expense was about 6d. per hole, including the spreading. Where it lay 9 feet as it frequently did in some parts of the Fens, it was not possible at that depth to obtain so much clay and the cost was from 10d. to 1s. for each hole.[23] The expense per acre worked out at about 50s,[24] but everyone agreed that it was worth while because the profit from the improved agriculture was so great. Crops such as cabbages, mangel-wurzels, potatoes, beans, etc., were grown in increasing quantities,[25] but the most important effect that claying had was on the corn crops. Instead of a very inferior crop of oats which often had to be left on the ground as the waters rose, now the farmers were able to produce good quality wheat. By claying, the straw became firm and strong and not so tall as formerly. The ear was larger and heavier, and the roots had a better hold in the soil so there was less liability to damage by wind or rain.[26] The result was that in some places the crops were doubled or even trebled,[27] but the produce was not always as great as that and the figures given by Mr Cooke are probably more representative:

	£.	s.	d.

1st. year. – in the original state of the soil the produce is 5 qrs. of oats, 10 stone gross at 20s. per qr. — 5. 0. 0.

2nd. year. – Seeds (herbage thereon), 4 sheep per acre at 3d. per head, from the 1st of April to the 1st. of October, — 1. 4. 0.

3rd. year. – 20 bushels of very light wheat, say 16 stone gross, if clean enough for seed, 50s. per qr. — 6. 5. 0.

————

£12. 9. 0.

1st. year. – after trenching, it produces 6 qrs. of oats per acre, 12 stone net, at 24s. per qr. — 7. 4. 0.

2nd. year. – Seeds (herbage thereon), 7 sheep per acre, at 3d. per head, from the 1st. of April to the 1st. of October, — 2. 2. 0.

3rd. year. – 30 bushels of wheat per acre, at 58s. per qr., 17½ stone nett, — 10. 17. 6.

————

£20. 3. 6.

[28]

Paring and burning was still necessary on those lands which could not be clayed or on new land which was being broken up for agriculture where the roots of reeds or rushes were too coarse to be broken up by the plough and would not decay during the summer.[29] In other places claying quickly spread throughout the whole of the Fens, and it became the regular custom to clay every six years.[30] Many farmers thought that if a little produced such good results, more would give even better, a certain Mr Wingate being among them.

With regard to the management of my own farm . . . it had been occupied before I took it by a tenant, and had been clayed all over once at my expense. . . . After that I clayed it again . . . after that it was sown with 1st. year Oats; 2nd. Wheat; 3rd. Cole with manure; 4th. Oats; 5th. Wheat; 6th. Cole or Turnips well manured and then clayed all over a third time same as before; and most certainly I had most productive crops, that is as much as 5 qrs. of wheat per acre, and from 8 to 9 qrs. of oats, all of very fair quality. I began to clay again the fourth time, but not with the same favourable results, and have only done some little over again, thinking the lands have got quite sufficient solidity.[31]

In some parts, the soil became almost too good so that farmers could grow wheat year after year, occasionally interspersed with oats.[32] Wheat became the predominant crop, and the effect of steam drainage and claying was that "the Middle and South Levels, from an oat-growing, became a wheat-growing country".[33]

The answers given to the Select Committee on Agricultural Distress in 1836 show that this change also took place in the northern parts of the Fens, for the two gentlemen questioned, Mr Joseph Cook Arnall, a corn inspector, and George Calthrop, a corn merchant, came from Boston and Spalding respectively. Their answers show that although the change from oats to wheat was fairly recent, it had become very widespread.

In a return which has been presented to the Committee containing an account of the number of quarters of wheat sold in certain markets of this kingdom, it appears that in Boston in the year 1829 there were 72,964 quarters of corn, and in 1834, 131,370; should you say that was a fair measure of comparison between those two years? – I should think that it is.

Then you consider that nearly double the quarters of wheat were sold in 1834 as in 1829? – There is a great deal more wheat grown in the fens of Lincolnshire than there used to be some years ago; the corn grown in the fens of Lincolnshire some years back was principally confined to oats; the land is brought into a better state of cultivation, and now the returns of oats have fallen off, and the returns of wheat considerably increased.[34]

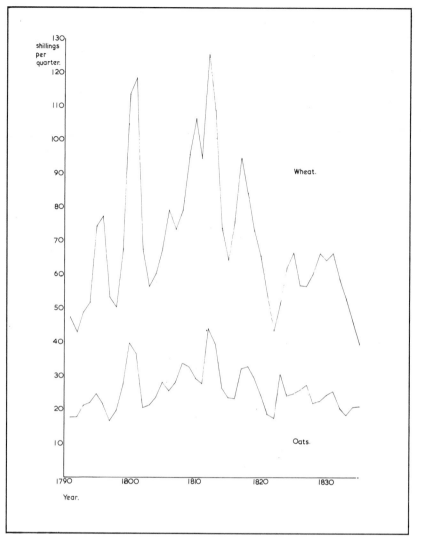

Price of Wheat and Oats 1791–1835

Within what period have they grown wheat in that district? – I think time out of mind, but formerly in a small quantity. It is a curious circumstance, I have heard my father say, that at Spalding they have been obliged to import wheat; and last year I myself exported 30,000 quarters of wheat from Spalding.

Has not the growth of wheat in your district progressively increased, and greatly increased even since the termination of the war? – No doubt of it.

How has that increase taken place? – The increase in our neighbourhood has chiefly taken place by land being reclaimed by drainage.

A large permanent outlay has been made upon it? – Such as I have stated before, there is one district of 34,000 acres drained by means of steam-engines for which an Act was passed in 1824, and the steam-engines were erected in 1826.[35]

The steam-engines to which Mr Calthrop referred were those erected in Deeping Fen. He remembered when that district was little better than a waste, but after the installation of the steam-engines it became admirable land in fine cultivation, producing immense crops of corn.[36]

132

The fen farmers not only could grow corn of a better quality, but they could use the land more intensively with more corn crops in their system of rotation. Mr Cooke's figures show how much more profitable it was to grow wheat rather than oats or leaving the land for pasture. It was no wonder that "some parts, which not many years ago were considered worth not more than seven pounds an acre to purchase, have been sold within the last five years at forty-five pounds an acre; while for others, a very few years since offered for a gallon of beer per acre, nearly forty pounds have been given".[37] Littleport Fen ceased to be a place "into which stock was turned amongst the reed and 'turf-bass', and not seen for days together", and became a country "teeming with the produce of corn, seeds, and coleseed".[38] The rent of Deeping Fen rose to an average of 35s. an acre and even £2, while land sold between £50 and £70 an acre.[39]

These great developments were taking place against a background of very unsettled conditions. The war years had provided a stimulus to draining and ploughing the Fens and everybody expected the boom to continue. So great had been the excitement caused by the prosperity during the war, that when hostilities ceased, and prices began to fall, neither owners nor occupiers could believe that the decrease would be anything but temporary. This belief was strengthened first by the Corn Laws which fixed the import price at 80s. a quarter, and then by the high prices of 1816 and 1817 caused by the wet harvest of the earlier year.[40] New rent agreements, often at an increased rental, were entered into on the assumption that the prices would remain at the same height, protected by the import duty. At the end of the Napoleonic Wars, rents were lower than the economic situation and profits really demanded, but as the position slowly deteriorated, rents remained the same with perhaps a small decrease after 1818 until by 1836 they were too high, especially when compared with the fall in prices.[41] The farmers' position was made more difficult because large quantities of foreign corn were imported during the scarce years. Great stocks of this remained in store, and the merchants had to sell it during the good years when the price was low with a further fall in price as the consequence.[42]

The interval up to 1834 included a series of adverse years increasing in pressure. Applications for reduction of rent and tithes became common and then followed failure and changes of occupancy without number.[43] Mr Calthrop thought that the farmer was thirty per cent worse off in 1836 than in 1818,[44] but it was partly the old story, those who adopted the new methods succeeded, while those who did not, went under. Mr Wingate, who so successfully applied clay to his farm, did not work it himself at this early period. The tenants followed the old method of paring and burning and were rewarded with very bad quality oats. They were nearly ruined, but when Mr Wingate took it over, the system of claying had been introduced, and the farm proved very successful with the new techniques.[45]

The new methods enabled the fen farmers to produce a wheat crop which had a greater yield per acre than any other area in England. Produce of other wheat lands was something under 24 bushels an acre but, in the Fens, the average yield for normal years was 28 to 30 bushels. During the years 1833 to 1836 the wheat harvest was exceptionally good and averaged 34 bushels per acre, which helped to bring down the price.[46] Mr Calthrop thought that the "immense tracts of land brought into wheat cultivation in the fens of Lincolnshire, and of Cambridgeshire and of Norfolk, have had a very great effect upon the price of wheat",[47] and Mr Arnall agreed that "this enormous increase in the quantity of wheat"[48] had affected the price, partly through the greater quantity grown, and partly through the abundance of the years since 1833. The price of wheat fell, but although this was to some extent counterbalanced by the gain in productivity, the farmer had to introduce improvements and use greater skill if he wished to remain solvent. As the farmers saw that they had to grow corn at lower prices, they made up their minds to do it by using more labour and more efficient methods. "Immediately after the war, the farmers declared that they could not grow wheat under £4 a quarter; then they reduced the price at which they thought they could grow it to 70s. and then to 60s.; they think now they could grow it very well at 60s., and even at 56s. or 55s."[49]

The fen farmers may have suffered through this fall in price, but other sections of the country benefited. The years 1833 to 1835 were undoubtedly years of over-production, but in the other years, the increase in demand from the growing industrial areas was just about balanced by the increase of wheat grown in the Fens. This was the period of the greatest rise in the birth-rate during the Industrial Revolution, and it was estimated that the population increased by five million between the censuses of 1821 and 1831. The gradual fall in the price of wheat showed that the demand had been met by increased production, and the bulk of this wheat seems to have come from the Fens, for there was not the same expansion in cultivation in other areas except the Wolds of Lincolnshire and Yorkshire.[50] The Fens, with their unrivalled water communications, were well placed to supply the growing industrial areas, and Mr Calthrop himself sent corn "chiefly to Yorkshire and to London; sometimes to the West coast, and sometimes to Newcastle and Scotland".[51] The older cultivated lands were unable to meet the demand, and supply the increasing manufacturing population with bread as well as "the increasing number of horses belonging to our luxurious population with oats".[52] At this period the Fens, protected by the Corn Laws, helped to fill the deficit through the introduction of better drainage aided by steam-engines.

NOTES

1. R. N. Bacon, *The Report on the Agriculture of Norfolk* (1844), p. 93.
2. J. A. Clarke, "The Great Level of the Fens", *J.R.A.S.*, vol. 8 (1847), p. 121.
3. G. Aikin, "Culture of the Cambridgeshire Fens", *Trans. Soc. of Arts*, vol. 52 (1838–9), p. 174.
4. J. Rennie, Letter Books, vol. 10, p. 6, 16 October 1818.
5. J. Glynn, "Draining Land by Steam Power", *Trans. Soc. of Arts*, vol. 51 (1838), p. 8.
6. J. A. Clarke, op. cit., p. 120.
7. J. A. Clarke, "On the Farming of Lincolnshire", vol. 12 (1851), p. 296.
8. J. A. Clarke, "The Great Level of the Fens", *J.R.A.S.*, vol. 8 (1847), p. 120.
9. S. Jonas, "On the Farming of Cambridgeshire", *J.R.A.S.*, vol. 7 (1846), p. 67.
10. G. D. Dempsey, *Rudimentary Treatise on Drainage . . .* (1854), p. 83.
11. G. Aikin, op. cit., p. 174.
12. S. Jonas, op. cit., pp. 71 ff. See also B. Almack, "On the Agriculture of Norfolk", *J.R.A.S.*, vol. 5 (1844), p. 311. R. N. Bacon, op. cit., p. 93. P. Pusey, "Some account of the Practise of English Farmers in the Improvement of Peaty Ground", *J.R.A.S.*, vol. 2 (1841), p. 406. S. Wells, *The History of the Drainage of . . . Bedford Level*, vol. 1 (1830), p. 442.
13. R. Parkinson, *Huntingdon* (1811), p. 301.
14. ibid., p. 299.
15. A. Young, *A. of A.*, vol. 36, p. 83.
16. ibid., p. 85.
17. P. Pusey, "On the Agricultural Improvements of Lincolnshire", *J.R.A.S.*, vol. 4 (1843), p. 292.
    This cheap transformation of the soil has been carried out with great spirit in the Lincolnshire Fens, since Mr. Young's Report; and as he does not speak of the process, the whole credit of it is due, I suppose, to the present generation of farmers.
18. S. Wells, op. cit., p. 442.
19. J. A. Clarke, "The Great Level of the Fens", *J.R.A.S.*, vol. 8 (1847), p. 92.
20. P. Pusey, "Some account of the Practise of English Farmers . . .", *J.R.A.S.*, vol. 2 (1841), p. 414.
21. B. Almack, op. cit., p. 311.
22. J. A. Clarke, "The Great Level of the Fens", *J.R.A.S.*, vol. 8 (1847), p. 95.
23. R. N. Bacon, op. cit., p. 94.
24. P. Pusey, "Some account of the Practise of English Farmers . . .", *J.R.A.S.*, vol. 2 (1841), p. 406, and B. Almack, op. cit., p. 311.
25. G. Aikin, op. cit., p. 177.

26. G. D. Dempsey, op. cit., p. 83.
27. P. Pusey, "Some account of the Practise of English Farmers . . .", *J.R.A.S.*, vol. 2 (1841), pp. 407 and 409.
28. ibid., p. 406.
29. ibid., p. 401.
30. ibid., p. 407.
31. ibid., p. 408.
32. S. Jonas, op. cit., p. 70.
33. J. A. Clarke, "The Great Level of the Fens", *J.R.A.S.*, vol. 8 (1847), p. 97.
34. *Minutes of Evidence Taken before Select Committee on Agricultural Distress, March 1836*, Questions 9602–3.
35. ibid., Questions 8115–19.
36. ibid., Questions 7990–4.
37. R. N. Bacon, op. cit., p. 18.
38. J. A. Clarke, "The Great Level of the Fens", *J.R.A.S.*, vol. 8 (1847), p. 95.
39. ibid., p. 119, see also G. D. Dempsey, op. cit., p. 83.
40. R. N. Bacon, op. cit., p. 95.
41. *Minutes of Evidence Taken before Select Committee on Agricultural Distress, March 1836*, Questions 7898–900.
42. ibid., Questions 7870–1.
    Have you ever imported wheat from Spain? – Yes in 1829.
    Is that not a very unusual source? – Yes, nothing but the high price in the English market tempted them to send it. I believe they were taking corn out of their stores of abundance.
43. R. N. Bacon, op. cit., p. 95.
44. *Minutes of Evidence Taken before Select Committee on Agricultural Distress, March 1836*, Questions 7793–4.
45. P. Pusey, "Some account of the Practise of English Farmers . . .", *J.R.A.S.*, vol. 2 (1841), p. 408.
46. *Minutes of Evidence Taken before Select Committee on Agricultural Distress, March 1836*, Questions 7881 and 7784–6.
47. ibid., Question 8005.
48. ibid., Questions 9605–6.
49. ibid., Question 8089.
50. ibid., Question 8141.
51. ibid., Question 7830.
52. T. Allen, *The History of the County of Lincoln* (1833), p. 54.

CHAPTER X

To Follow Where Improvement Leads

The years immediately following 1840 were an age of golden prosperity for the Fens. As the population in the rest of Britain continued to increase, so did the demand for food. The acreage of land drained by steam-engines steadily expanded, and the writers in the *Journal of the Royal Agricultural Society* confidently expected that windmills "would not be left for long, for almost every time the Commissioners meet, orders are given for pulling down another mill".[1] In his tour through the Fens, Jonas travelled from Wisbech to March and passed through "a district of splendid fen land, a portion of which is still drained by wind-mills. . . . I must express my great surprise that land of so much value should be left to the uncertainty of this power. I feel no doubt but that in a few years we shall see nothing but steam engines used for that purpose."[2]

A further boost to the fenland economy was given by the construction of railway lines. The first line of major importance was the Cambridge to Ely and King's Lynn which at last connected the Fens directly to London. In Ely Cathedral there is a tablet entitled the "Spiritual Railway" which is a memorial to two workmen who died on 24 December 1845 while helping to build this line. A glance at a map will show the extensive network of lines which extended across this area and helped to carry away fenland agricultural produce to the large cities. Today most of the sidings and many of the lines that served the farmers have been taken up, and even the one laid especially for sugar-beet, the Wissington Light Railway near Stoke Ferry, has been abandoned. Although the farmers may have benefited from faster and more reliable transport, the Drainage Boards which had derived a sizeable portion of their income from tolls on river craft suffered a severe diminution in their revenue. The toll receipts of the Waterbeach Level fell from £250 in 1840 to £60 ten years later. A similar decrease occurred on the River Witham where the Railway Company had bought out the River Navigation, for soon the tolls diminished to such an extent that they did not pay for the upkeep. Today the railway line itself has been closed and taken up.

Improved access to larger markets stimulated the farmers into experiments with a greater variety of crops than just cole seed and corn. During this golden period a few people began to grow root crops such as turnips, carrots and swedes, and also potatoes, but the main crop remained corn, principally wheat. Steam drainage made it worth while enclosing and cultivating every little bit of fenland so that the indigenous marsh plants began to disappear, for with windmills the land remained wet enough to enable them to survive. Those plants which depended upon the dampness of the atmosphere for their survival, such as the Marsh Fern, quickly vanished from the greater part of the area, but those which lived in water remained in the drains and ditches. The roots of reeds still remain in the drains and are a menace to the farmer, for in a wet season they spread into the fields and cause considerable damage. Another scourge was the twitch or couch grass, which grew very quickly in the peaty soil. Gangs of women and children were employed to pull it out of the fields, sometimes under rather grim conditions as the reports of the Children Employment Commission revealed only too clearly.

As the last quarter of the century approached, the farmers found that black clouds began to appear on the horizon. The steam-engine which had brought prosperity to the Fens began to take it away again. The steam-engine which had pumped the land dry and then provided transport by water and rail had been developed further, so that it conquered the oceans. Also the railways were opening up new continents so that the fen farmer found himself competing with corn from America and Canada which was much cheaper than his own. The protecting Corn Laws had been swept away, and the powerful manufacturing interests wanted cheap food to feed their masses of employees. The Fens entered a period of deep depression from which they did not recover until the First World War.

The depression started between 1875 and 1879, and was attributed first and foremost to a succession of four or five years of bad harvests due to wet seasons which seriously affected the wheat crops. Then the recent Education Acts had limited the employment of children so that one source of cheap labour was denied to the farmer. These other causes, in addition to foreign competition, caused a severe depression in the Fens, especially as wheat was still the staple product. There was general and widespread distress among the farmers "one half of whom were absolutely insolvent, and the other half greatly reduced in circumstances".[3] In 1880 and 1881 there followed further bad harvests, but in the later 1880s the position began to ease a little because there was a change to potatoes which proved "the mainstay of the Fen farmer".[4] Other crops such as mustard helped, for the Fens were endowed with a natural fertility which seemed to be almost inexhaustible, and this prevented their being as hard hit as many other areas.

This period of depression had a profound effect on the steam-engine that drained the land. Economy became all important. This can be seen first of all in the wages of the men who worked them. Compared with our present time, the nineteenth century was a period of remarkable stability, so it is worth while turning aside to look at the men who looked after these engines. Each drainage area employed its own people to keep the banks in order, the drains and ditches clean, and the engines and bridges repaired. The local landowners would serve as Commissioners and were the ultimate source of authority. Under them would be a Clerk, responsible for collecting the drainage taxes and conducting any legal or large financial transactions. A Superintendent or Surveyor would be appointed for supervising the work within the Level itself. He would employ such men as might be needed to maintain the works and run the engines. In the larger districts, there would be engineers under the Superintendent to work the steam-engines, but in the smaller districts such as the Waterbeach Level, the Superintendent would be his own engineer. In Deeping Fen the person in charge of the engines, Mawson, was paid £200 per annum, but he had to find his own labourers.[5] The man who erected the steam-engine often remained to work it. Mawson came from Leeds where one of the Pode Hole engines was built, and his successor, John Tricket, put up the Butterley engine. It is not known whether Jonathen Stanley (1833–40) or his successor Edwin Stanley (1840–80) at the Stretham engine had any connexion with the Butterley Company which built it, but their successors, Henry Walters (1880–4) and Isaac Housley (1884–1930), both had been employed by that company. Jonathen Stanley was responsible for ordering and buying the coal but, after he left, the Clerk assumed this duty. In addition to their regular pay, a donation might be made for any special work, such as a long spell of continuous pumping during a flood, and Edwin Stanley's widow was paid a gratuity of £40. On the other hand, Henry Walters died suddenly, leaving a deficit of £13 in his accounts, so his lathe was seized in lieu of repayment and it still remains in the engine-house. These superintendents had their house and coal free in addition to their pay.

The only other regularly paid employee when the engine was first installed at Stretham was the mole-catcher. He had a vital task to prevent the moles making holes through the banks, thus weakening the structure and letting water through in a flood. One regular stoker was given a free house and coal, but at first he was not employed all the time, only when the engine was running. Presumably he found other casual work on the farms to supplement his income which varied considerably from year to year. Later he was employed on a more definite basis, as the Agreement of 1900 shows.

Engineer's Agreement with Stoker, 12 November 1900.

1st. One month's notice to be given or taken by either party.
2nd. The working time (when engine is running) to be 12 hours per day; other days from 6.30 a.m. to 5.0 p.m.
3rd. Duties, to work at Engine, on the Level, and do anything required by the Engineer.
4th. Wages to be 14/– per week with House and Coal One month's absence to be allowed for Harvest when not required to assist at repairs.[6]

Should the stoker have to work at the engine over harvest-time, he was paid double, and this applied to anyone else who had to help with repairs at the same time. All the other work in the Level was done by contracts or casual labour. The same people were employed time and time again, but apparently on no regular basis. During periods of continuous pumping, other men would be engaged to help the stoker, but not regularly, while the proper stoker worked on the banks or ditches during the summer. When the engine was running, there were the boilers which needed constant replenishment with fuel, and in addition all the bearings of the engine had to be lubricated and topped-up every hour. This must have been a difficult and dangerous job at night, when the unguarded machinery was lit only by tallow candles. The stoker was provided with a special waterproof oilskin, so he could go inside the wheel-house and pour pitch on the gear-wheels to keep them lubricated. He had another unpleasant task, which was chipping off the scale that formed inside the boilers. This must have been particularly dirty and arduous, confined inside the narrow spaces of the boilers.

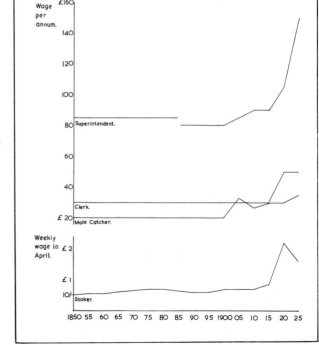

Waterbeach Level wages taken at five-yearly intervals

138

Some of these men remained many years at the same engines. Edwin Stanley and Housley together worked at the Stretham engine for a total of eighty-six years. The Stevens family gave faithful service at the Hundred Foot engine, son succeeding father, and there were similar instances in other parts of the Fens. The accompanying table shows the wages paid to their regular employees by the Waterbeach Level Commissioners. The effect of the agricultural depression in the 1880s is well illustrated by the fall in wages at that time. After Walters had died in 1884, the Commissioners offered the post of Superintendent at £75 per annum, but could find no one willing to take it and were forced to accept Housley's suggestion of £80. Wages had begun to rise again by the beginning of the new century, and the First World War seriously dislocated the labour market, so labour costs shot up and did not return to the pre-war levels. This rise in wages, imposed on top of the agricultural depression, made the Commissioners look for every possible economy, both in capital expenditure and daily charges. If a new engine had to be erected, then it had to be constructed cheaply, while greater economy was sought in maintaining and running existing engines.

If the weight of the engines and scoopwheels could be reduced, then the cost of building the engine-houses would also be lowered, especially where the foundations were bad. People tried many different types of engines in an endeavour to save weight. Glynn experimented with a side-lever engine at Middle Fen, Prickwillow, in 1833. He described it as a "Marine type" engine which was lighter than the conventional beam-engine because a smaller beam was placed below the vertical cylinder, thus dispensing with the pillars, entablature and long connecting-rod.[7] The foundations here were bad and the engine had to be built on piles driven through the peat into the clay. It developed 60 h.p. and drained 7,000 acres by a scoopwheel, 33 feet 6 inches in diameter by 2 feet 1 inch wide.

The grasshopper-engine was developed from the beam-engine and became quite popular in the Fens because it was lighter. Examples were built at Chettisham near Ely and Whittlesey, to name but two, although the conventional beam-engine and scoopwheel continued to be the standard engine design until long after 1855 when the other surviving steam-engine in the Fens, the Tattershall engine at Dog Dyke, was built. While the slowly revolving scoopwheel was used to lift the water, the ideal power unit was the low-pressure condensing beam-engine, but in 1852 the first of a different type of pump was used to drain Whittlesey Mere.

Whittlesey Mere was the last of the great sheets of water that had been common all over the Fens. Many people enjoyed sailing and fishing there, and, if the winter was cold enough, it was often the scene of skating championships. As the drainage in the other parts of the Middle Level improved, it was felt that it was dangerous to have this large volume of water in the higher part of the district which would cause a severe flood in the event of a bank breaking. In 1851 a cut was made through the surrounding bank and the water flowed freely for several days into the exterior river. But after the first rush of water had subsided, it became clear that a perfectly natural drainage could not be maintained because the winter level of the water outside rose above the bed of the Mere. It was obvious that some form of pumping was necessary, and it was decided to install the centrifugal pump which had been so successfully demonstrated at the Great Exhibition.

Accordingly there was erected one of Easton and Amos's horizontal-spindle centrifugal Appold pumps, capable of discharging 16,000 gallons per minute against a 6-foot lift, driven by a 25 h.p. beam-engine.[8] Throughout the summer of 1852, much progress was made in bringing the bed of the Mere into a fit state for cultivation, in laying out roads and drains, and in planning farms. But during the autumn, heavy rains swelled the rivers and the pressure on the banks was so great that, on 2 November, the banks burst and in

Independent type of engine at Little Thetford, showing how the beam is supported on an "A" frame (B. and W. Coll.)

Scoopwheel of the Little Thetford engine (B. and W. Coll.)

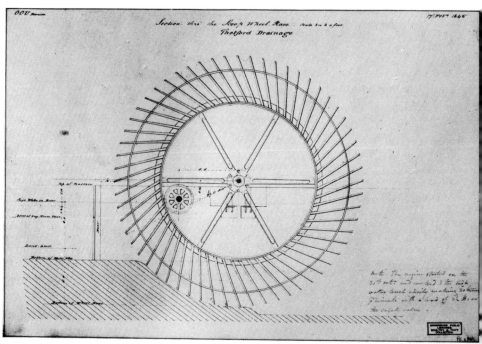

An overhead beam type of grasshopper at West Butterwick, showing the bevel drive to the centrifugal pump (R.H.C.)

Coates engine; this grasshopper type has the crank near the floor and the beam at the top of the engine (R.H.C.)

Left: *Detail of the top of the cylinder and connecting rod of one of the Lade Bank engines (R.H.C.)*

Right: *Chettisham engine grasshopper type with low beam and overhead crank (R.H.C.)*

Far right: *A very small vertical engine at Middleton (R.H.C.)*

Below: *General view of the Lade Bank engines which drove vertical spindle centrifugal pumps (R.H.C.)*

a few hours Whittlesey Mere was itself again. About 1,000 acres were covered with 2½ feet of water, so the new pump was worked continuously for three weeks until the Mere was dry again. The following summer, cole seed and Italian rye grass were the crops taken, and afterwards oats and wheat were successfully planted. The mean annual value of the Mere before drainage was £1,160 and after £12,350.[9]

From this pump other forms of centrifugal and later turbine-pumps were developed, but many people in the Fens still preferred the scoopwheel, believing it to be superior to all other machines.[10] Controversy raged for many years because the position was complicated by the shrinkage of the fenland. At Whittlesey Mere, the average lift for the first few years was 4 or 5 feet, but by 1875 the peat had shrunk so much that it was 9 feet. Before drainage was commenced, an iron pillar was driven into the ground until the top was level with the surface, and today this rises at least 12 feet out of the ground. "This extraordinary and unlooked for subsidence of the land and consequent increase of lift has been most embarrassing and has caused Mr. Wells the proprietor a very serious expense to protect his tenants."[11] He had twice to lengthen the inlet pipe and lower the pump and in 1877 he installed a more powerful engine and vertical-spindle pump.[12] The greater lift decreased the volume of water that the old engine could pump, so the land was not as well drained, and many people argued from this that the pumps were not as efficient as the scoopwheels. If Whittlesey Mere had been drained by a scoopwheel new machinery would have been necessary, whereas it was a simple operation to lower the pump. The extent to which a scoopwheel could be lowered was limited by the meshing of the gear-wheels, and even where it was possible to lower the wheel, the expense was very great because the

143

foundations had to be rebuilt and the masonry trough reshaped to follow the lower curve of the wheel. The starts and ladles could be lengthened but even that was costly because the wheel-trough had to be altered. Most scoopwheels were enlarged or lowered once or sometimes twice during their working life. At the Swaffham and Bottisham engine the wheel was increased from 26 to 36 feet, and the Stretham engine wheel was enlarged from about 28 feet to 33 feet 6 inches by lengthening the starts and then a new wheel was installed over 37 feet in diameter. The same process happened at the Hundred Foot engine, where the wheel began at 35 feet, was enlarged to about 40 feet and a new one reached 50 feet, the largest in the Fens.

The scoopwheel had the advantage that it was simple to operate, cheap to maintain, and wasted less lifting power because the water was carried in the same direction and not swirled around as in the centrifugal pump. The scoopwheel pumped out more water per revolution when the drains were full, and so it lowered the water-level for the first few inches very quickly. This sometimes helped to save a crop and seemed to many farmers to be more important than throwing out the same quantity whether the water was high or low in the drain.[13] However, the economic factors could not be disregarded. For a new installation, the centrifugal pump was cheaper because it was smaller and did not need such heavy foundations or such a large building to protect it from the weather, but in 1877 a Mr Lunn's opinion was that

where the persons interested do not object to the *larger amount* of first cost involved by the erection of scoopwheels, and where the lift is not liable to variation and does not exceed eight feet, scoopwheels are as efficient as centrifugal pumps and are preferable on account of their being, in his opinion, simpler to manage and less liable to wear and tear.[14]

Gradually the centrifugal pumps became more popular, and in 1867 they were used to drain the East, West and Wildmore Fens. Although the drainage of these areas had been perfectly satisfactory for many years after the improvements carried out by John Rennie, the ground had slowly shrunk until "about 15,000 acres in the West Fen, and 25,000 acres in the East Fen, were in all winters imperfectly drained, and in winters of more than ordinary rainfall, about one half of these areas was submerged".[15] During the winter of 1866 the East Fen was for weeks under water, and looked from the neighbouring hills like a great lake.[16] Some farmers had installed their own temporary steam-pumps, but many felt that these only aggravated the problem because they raised the water in the main drains. Accordingly consent was obtained from Parliament to build a new pumping station at Hobhole Sluice to the designs of Mr Hawkshaw. Two sets of machinery were installed, each consisting of a high-pressure condensing vertical-cylinder steam-engine (cylinder 30 inches in diameter by 30 inches stroke) driving an Appold vertical-spindle centrifugal pump (7 feet in diameter by 2 feet 2 inches width). They were built by Easton, Amos and Anderson at a cost of £17,000. In the winter following their completion, there was an excessive rainfall. "Where as in January 1867, with a rainfall of 3·32 inches, an area computed at from 10,000 to 12,000 acres was placed under water for several weeks, the new machinery, in the month of December, 1870, with a rainfall of 5·28 inches, had kept the whole district perfectly clear."[17]

Mr Hawkshaw had been concerned a little before this with the drainage of the Middle Level. In May 1862 the Middle Level main sluice had blown up and a large area was flooded. It was obvious that the sluice could not be repaired before the floods of the following winter, so Hawkshaw proposed building a dam in place of the sluice and carrying the water over the top by means of siphons. Sixteen of these siphons were built, each 150 feet in length and 3 feet 6 inches in interior diameter.

144

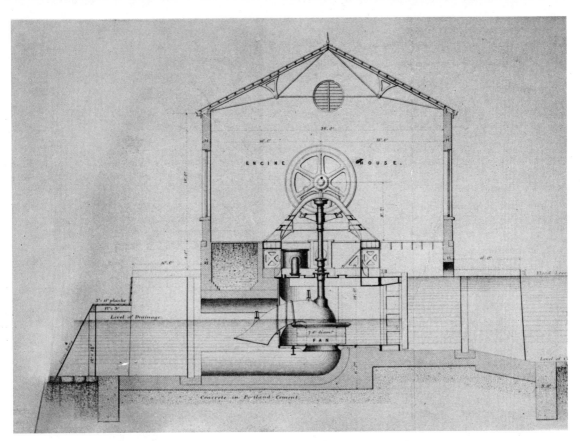

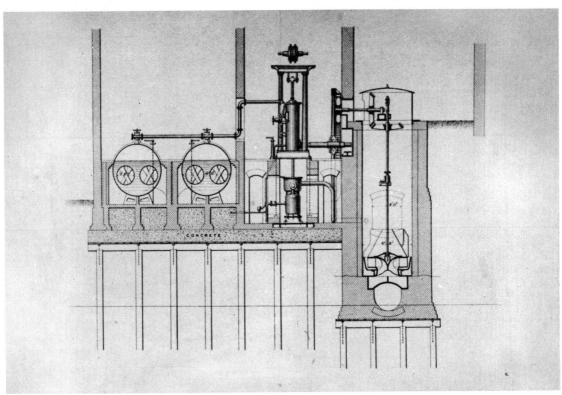

Design for Steam Engine and Centrifugal Pumps at Hobhole Sluice 1867

In the centre of the dam, a 9 inch pipe enters each syphon, and is furnished with a stop valve; it connects the syphons with an elevated pipe running transversely over them, which is connected with three air pumps, in an engine house on the west bank, by which the syphons are exhausted of air. . . . The air pumps are 15 inches in diameter, 18 inches in stroke, and are worked from a three-throw crank, impelled by a ten-horse engine, manufactured by Messrs. Easton and Amos.[18]

The idea did not work very well because air was drawn in with the water and collected at the top of the pipes. Unless this was frequently drawn out, the pipes stopped working, but the experiment filled the need for a temporary stopgap.

An interesting comparison of the performances of a centrifugal pump and a scoopwheel can be made because, in 1880, a 60 h.p. compound condensing beam-engine driving a vertical-spindle centrifugal pump was installed alongside the old 60 h.p. side-lever engine at Prickwillow. The new engine had two cylinders (high pressure 15 inches × 3 feet 1½ inches and low pressure 25 inches × 4 feet 6 inches) and drove a pump with a fan 5 feet 4 inches in diameter. Against a lift of 15 feet the pump made 128 r.p.m. to 38 of the engine. The cost of the new installation was £4,917,[19] which worked out at about £72 per horse-power, and the tables show that it was more efficient. Another great advantage of the centrifugal pump was that as the lift decreased, the quantity of water discharged automatically increased without any sensible alteration in the speed of the engine and without any care on the part of the Engineer.[20]

PRICKWILLOW, EXPERIMENTS ON OLD ENGINE, 19 JULY 1880

lbs. steam	R.P.M.	Lift	Water lifted per min.	Effective H.P.	Indicated H.P.	Efficiency
6	25·5	9′ 8¼″	73·0 tons	48·02	108·7	0·442
6	24·5	9′ 9¼″	73·0	48·41	103·4	0·468
6	24·5	9′ 9½″	70·9	47·11	103·7	0·454
6	23·5	9′ 10¾″	68·9	46·30	97·7	0·475

NEW ENGINE AND CENTRIFUGAL PUMP, 3 JULY 1880

lbs. steam	R.P.M.	Lift	Water lifted per min.	Effective H.P.	Indicated H.P.	Efficiency
66	31·1	9′ 7″	74·18	48·24	90·34	0·534
65	32·2	10′ 0½″	82·80	56·43	107·70	0·525
65	32·8	10′ 4½″	82·80	58·28	108·30	0·546
61	32·7	10′ 8″	74·18	53·73	102·40	0·527
63	33·0	10′ 11″	74·18	54·99	103·30	0·532
67	34·0	11′ 10″	74·18	59·57	114·60	0·519
67	35·4	12′ 5½″	69·20	58·41	116·00	0·504

Newer types of engine which were being developed with high-pressure steam and faster revolutions were more suitable for driving the centrifugal pump. The horizontal engine, which no longer necessitated any form of beam, was sometimes coupled to a scoopwheel, for example at Fiskerton. At March West Fen, a horizontal engine replaced a beam-engine and turned the old scoopwheel. This was repeated at other places in the Fens, but it did not make adequate use of the small size of these newer engines and the centrifugal pump. In some cases full advantage was taken and at Waldersea a small wooden building was built to house an inclined-cylinder condensing engine which augmented the older Cornish engine. The final developments along these lines were the Gwynne pumps and marine

A *Waldersea, looking along the top of the inclined cylinder. Note the way the valve cover is split (R.H.C.)*

B *Waldersea showing cross-head and disc-crank. This engine drove a vertical spindle centrifugal pump (R.H.C.)*

C *A typical example of a horizontal engine from Reedham in Norfolk (R.H.C.)*

D *Another view of the Reedham engine (R.H.C.)*

engines which replaced the Hundred Foot and Ten Mile Bank engines just before the First World War. The new 400 h.p. engine and pump comfortably fitted inside the old building which originally housed the 80 h.p. Hundred Foot engine. At the other end of the scale, centrifugal pumps were coupled to portable or semi-portable engines. Fowells, Tuxfords, Savages, and others built engines of this type which were used for the drainage of small areas. Some of the windmills had pulleys attached so that their scoopwheels could be worked by portable engines when there was no wind,[21] and the Cambridge firm of Swann Hurrell tried to install a steam-engine actually inside a windmill but it collapsed on top of them.[22]

Most of the other engines were altered to increase their efficiency and bring them into line with more modern practice. When the scoopwheel had to be deepened, or lowered through the shrinkage of the land, the opportunity was often taken to improve its performance. On the inlet side of the wheel, the drains and side walls were enlarged or rebuilt to improve the flow of water to the wheel, and at the outlet various ideas were adopted to ease the stream of water into the river. All scoopwheels had one or two doors fitted in front of them to prevent the water running back into the fen when pumping had ceased. In a high flood the ladles churned up a great quantity of water in front and created a strong back undercurrent which was so fierce at one engine that it sucked a small boat down to the cill and smashed it against the ladles.[23] Under these conditions the wheel absorbed a great deal of engine power because it became choked and could not discharge its water freely. A simple remedy was to cut the door, or doors, in front of the wheel horizontally in half so that when the water-level in the river was high, the bottom door would remain shut and the water flowed over the top. The exit of water into the river was further helped by streamlining the outfall drain so that there were no projections or sharp bends which could cause eddies.

Another improvement which greatly helped the performance was the adoption of a "rising breast" in front of the wheel. This was a sliding panel, curved to fit the radius of the wheel and worked by gearing inside the engine-house. Its effect was to raise or lower the delivery cill so that the height could be adjusted to correspond with the level of water in the river. One, installed at the Hundred Foot engine in 1872, could be raised 8 feet above the fixed masonry cill, and this gave a lift of 18 feet from the bottoms of the ladles to the top of the rising breast. Trials were carried out and a temporary weir, equal in height to a high flood-level in the river, was fixed across the outlet channel at a sufficient distance to allow the water to get well away from the wheel.

Steam during the trial was kept at a uniform pressure of 5 lb. in the boilers. The dip of the scoops was 3 feet 5 inches, and the head 15 feet 11 inches. With the movable breast down the engine was not able to raise the water over the dam, but came to a standstill. The movable breast was then raised four feet, when the engine made 4 revolutions a minute; when raised to five feet, the number increased to 12; at 6 feet, to 13; at 7 feet, to $13\frac{1}{2}$; and at 8 feet, or 18 feet above the tips of the scoops, the engine made nearly 14 revolutions per minute, and discharged over the dam a stream of water 7 feet 6 inches wide by 1 foot 8 inches deep.[24]

This clearly demonstrated the saving that these rising breasts achieved, and an improved version was fitted at the Pode Hole engines. There were the same curved iron breast-plates which fitted the radius of the wheel, but to the top of the breast there was fixed a wooden platform which slid into an iron frame. The lower end of the iron frame was fixed to the floor of the outlet channel by hinges so that when the breast was wound right down, the wooden platform and iron frame lay along the bottom of the outlet drain, but when the breast was raised, they formed an inclined plane down which the water could flow

SECTION

PLAN

SCOOP WHEEL AT PODEHOLE.

Pode Hole scoopwheel, W. H. Wheeler, Drainage of Fens . . . (1888), showing a "slacker" on the drain side and a "rising breast" on the river side

smoothly. This entirely avoided the back current at the bottom of the outlet which always existed in the old arrangement.

A further alteration at the Pode Hole engines which greatly increased the efficiency was the addition of a shuttle on the inlet side of the wheels. This regulated the amount of water coming to the wheel and enabled the wheel to be kept fully charged without being drowned. The shuttle consisted of a wooden sluice across the inlet at an angle of forty-five degrees to the bottom of the raceway. It was fixed quite close to the wheel and was the same width. It was counterbalanced by an iron weight hung by a chain running over a pulley, and could be raised or lowered by gearing from inside the engine-house.

The water passing under the shuttle does not catch the scoops until they come towards the bottom of the trough, and then impinges on them in the same direction in which they are travelling, and with a velocity due to the head of water at the back of the door [shuttle], and thus aiding the forward motion of the wheel. The scoops become fully charged as they assume a vertical position. The apparent increase in the lift from the lower level from which the water has to be raised is more than compensated for by the avoidance of the mass of dead water which a wheel has generally to encounter on first entering the water, and by the wheel being just sufficiently fed with water having a velocity and direction which assist in sending it round. A much greater quantity of water is thus raised with the same amount of steam than could be done if the shuttle were not there.[25]

149

A shuttle was fitted on the Hundred Foot engine, but it does not seem to have been in general use for normal working. Shuttles were useful in adjusting the load when first starting, before the wheel had got into full swing. It was suggested that one should be fitted to the Stretham engine in 1893 when the gear-wheels were discovered to be badly worn.[26] Some of the strain would have been taken off the teeth when starting as the engine would not have to move all the dead water in the drain. It was never fitted as the whole wheel and gearing was renewed in 1896. Shuttles also controlled the depth of immersion of the scoops and prevented overloading. Where the river was tidal, the supply of water could be adjusted to compensate for the rising tide.

At the same time as the scoopwheels were being improved, the beam-engines that drove them were being altered. The original "wagon" type boilers with fires underneath them wore out and were replaced by the Cornish or Lancashire types which had furnaces contained in tubes inside them. Instead of only 4 lbs. per square inch, these new boilers could be worked at a much higher pressure which helped to save coal and gave the engines greater power. The full potential of this increase could not be realized until the valve gear of the engines had been reconstructed. Most of the early engines were built with "D" slide valves without any variable cut-off. This meant that the speed of the engine was controlled by the regulator and not by the cut-off. The opening of the exhaust valves to the condenser was too short and the valve ports were inadequate so that the engines wasted a great deal of steam. With higher boiler pressures, these troubles were accentuated.

In order to achieve more economical working, most of the engines in the Fens were given some form of variable expansion valve gear during their long working lives. Many were altered in the 1880s during the time of agricultural depression, because the increase in power and great savings in fuel meant that the district had virtually a new engine for very little expense. Between 1878 and 1884 James Watt and Company rebuilt the valve gears of all the Deeping Fen and Littleport and Downham engines. The Ten Mile Bank engine was altered first[27] and in 1881 the Hundred Foot engine was overhauled and refitted. Extra power was needed for the scoopwheels were enlarged at the same time. Piston valves were substituted for the slide valves, and hand-regulated internal expansion valves were added which could be used to vary the cut-off from one-tenth to one-half. The boiler pressure was raised at the same time to 20 lbs. and this gave the Hundred Foot engine an indicated horse-power of 224.

Similar alterations were carried out on the Pode Hole engines, and new boilers, totalling five in number, were provided to work at a pressure of 20 lbs. There was a considerable saving in coal at all these engines. At the Hundred Foot engine, the consumption for 1881 was 1,411 tons for 2,988 hours working at an average dip of 2·66 feet. After the improvements, the average dip in 1883 was 3·30 for 2,288 hours running, and, allowing for the difference in the number of hours, there was a clear saving of 369 tons of coal in one season, while the average extra head pumped against was increased by 1·54 feet. This gave an increase in work of 31 per cent and decrease of coal of 35 per cent. At Pode Hole the coal consumption was reduced from 5 tons 9 cwt. to 3 tons 28 cwt. per day, or 60 per cent more water was raised with 42 per cent less fuel. At this station the annual saving was estimated at £450 in wet seasons.[28] In 1915 the total discharge of these wheels was 563 tons per minute, and the cost of raising 570 tons of water was only "one penny for fuel costs, which is hard to surpass with modern plant".[29]

Examples could be given of similar alterations to engines throughout the Fens. Pinchbeck Spalding Marsh engine now has a Worthington-Simplex piston valve in place of its old valves, and in 1850 the Swaffham and Bottisham engine was altered and possibly completely renewed.[30] It may have received further changes after that, for in the 1930s the

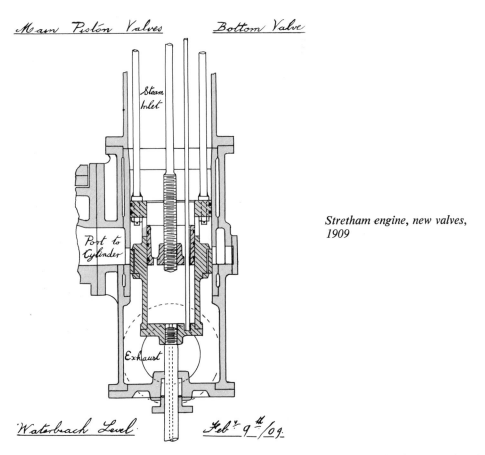

Main Piston Valves   *Bottom Valve*

Steam Inlet

Port to Cylinder

Exhaust

Waterbeach Level   *Feb.y 9th/09.*

Stretham engine, new valves, 1909

horse-power was rated at 50 and the steam-pressure had been raised to 35. The photographs that survive seem to show that the greater part of the first engine was retained and so worked for well over a hundred years until 1939. Then one day as the Engineer was stopping, having drawn the fires and let the boiler pressure right down, he gave the engine a quarter-turn backwards to close the doors of the scoopwheel to the river. The bottom pivot of the doors gave way and water began to pour into the Fen. The only way to stop the water was to throw bags full of sand into the outfall, but these smashed the scoopwheel and it was decided not to repair the damage but to scrap the engine.

At the Stretham engine, the boiler pressure was raised to only 8 lbs. in 1888 and a rising breast was fitted in 1897 after a new scoopwheel had been installed. These alterations gave some economy in coal, for 1 ton burnt for 4·3 hours compared with the previous figure of 4 hours. Otherwise this engine remained virtually in its original condition until 1909, but by that time seventy years of use had made the slide valves leak badly. One Engineer inspected the engine and recommended new valves, a new steel cylinder without a steam-jacket, and various other structural alterations which would have necessitated moving the condenser tank.[31] Housley, the Superintendent in charge of the engine, drew up his own plans for new piston valves only. The main valves were still worked by the existing eccentric, but the beam drove a second set of piston valves inside the others. The setting of these could be varied by hand in order to control the cut-off of the steam going into the cylinder. The main valves alone opened the exhaust portion of the stroke, and in this way it was possible to vary the admission of steam to the cylinder while the exhaust to the condenser remained open as long as possible. The valve ports were enlarged as much as was safe, but they still constricted the flow of steam a little.

151

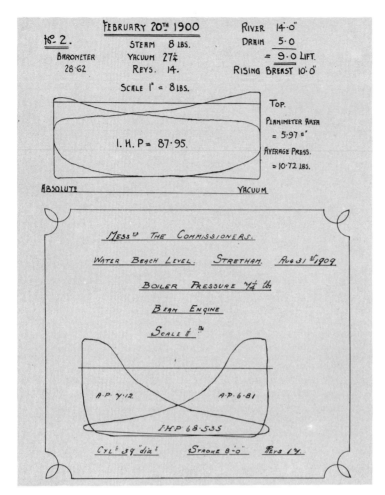

Stretham engine indicator diagrams

The new valves and gear put in by Messrs. Petrie and Co. are very satisfactory. The Committee of inspection examined the work and saw the engine at work. Last Saturday, Oct. 2nd, the engine ran splendidly six hours. It is now practically noiseless.

Being new, these valves do not work as freely as they will after working six months, and they want some little easing with a file, otherwise they are a very good job, not showing any signs of a leak. I submit a few diagrams . . . which I took on August 31st. These are quite equal to diagrams obtained from the latest modern Corliss Trip valve gear costing about £1,200 and show the engine giving off 68·53 Horse Power cutting off steam at Two Tenths. At $4\frac{3}{4}$ cut-off, it will develop 105 Horse Power. The greatest load in any flood of which we have record was in February 1900, when 87 Horse Power was given off with the river at 14 feet, drain at 5 feet, lift 9 feet.

Advantages:—

1) Present cylinder retained and fit for another 50 years service.

2) Reduction in cost of packing.

3) Reduction of coal 15 to 25 per cent, and in this connection I may add we have yet to find out the best system of firing the boilers to suit altered conditions.

4) About one half of the injection water is required for condensing. This means less work for the Air Pump.[32]

These new valves cost £350 and, in addition, Housley received £20 as a donation. The coal consumption was reduced by a third to about 1 ton for every 6 hours running.

After the First World War, the boilers were almost past further repair and suggestions were made for replacing them with new steel ones with a pressure of 25 lbs. In 1921 Gwynnes sent an estimate for one of their pumps, worked by a Galloway patent uniflow engine, which with boiler and engine-house would have cost £10,100.[33] Coal consumption would have been about 3 cwt. per hour. Inquiries about a diesel-engine showed that this new form of power would cost much less. A 184 b.h.p. Mirrlees four-cylinder diesel-engine cost only £2,290,[34] and about the same had to be paid for a Gwynne pump. On 20 February 1925 this engine had a trial run for $3\frac{1}{4}$ hours, "everything satisfactory except Air Pump. Drain empty. To do this work, the old engine must have run 11 hours."[35]

As their boilers became unsafe, one steam-engine after another was replaced by the more compact diesel- or petrol-engine. Today electric pumps are replacing the internal combustion engines for they can be controlled automatically by the water-level in the drains. Meanwhile, the Stretham engine was retained as a stand-by engine for use in emergencies.

Layout for adapting a beam-engine to drive a screw-pump

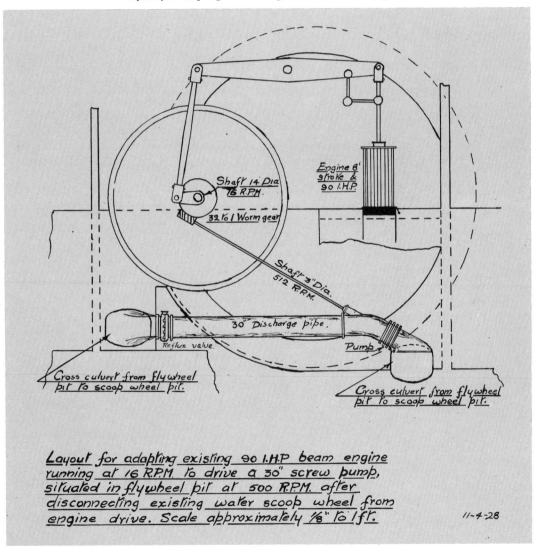

153

In 1928 the starts on the scoopwheel needed repair, so Housley made inquiries about replacing the scoopwheel with some form of impeller pump. Considerable cost would have been involved and so nothing was changed. The engine and scoopwheel were overhauled and last worked on 11 March 1941. Later the scoopwheel door to the river became rotten so it was concreted up in 1953 and now the engine cannot do any useful work. However, the Stretham Engine Preservation Trust hope that steam may again be raised and the engine run to show people one of the engines which for over a hundred years made such an important contribution to the draining of the Fens.

NOTES

1. J. A. Clarke, "The Great Level of the Fens", *J.R.A.S.*, vol. 8 (1847), p. 93.
2. J. A. Clarke, "On the Farming of Cambridgeshire", *J.R.A.S.*, vol. 7 (1846), p. 69.
3. H. C. Darby, *The Draining of the Fens* (1940), p. 246.
4. ibid., p. 248.
5. Deeping Fen Minutes, 4 August 1825.
6. Stretham Engine Records.
7. J. Glynn, "Draining Land by Steam Power", *Trans. Soc. of Arts*, vol. 51 (1836).
8. S. H. Miller and S. B. J. Sketchly, *Fenland Past and Present* (1878), p. 163.
9. ibid., p. 165.
10. W. H. Wheeler, *The Drainage of Fens* . . . (1888), p. 50.
11. J. M. Heathcote, *Scoopwheel and Centrifugal Pump* (1877), p. 12.
12. L. Gibbs, "Pumping Machinery in the Fenland and by the Trent-side", *Min. Proc. Inst. Civ. Eng.*, vol. XCIV (1888), p. 277.
13. J. M. Heathcote, op. cit., p. 4.
14. ibid., p. 10.
15. T. Hawksley, *Min. Proc. Inst. Civ. Eng.*, vol. XXXIV (1872), p. 138.
16. S. H. Miller and S. B. J. Sketchly, op. cit., p. 151.
17. T. Hawksley, op. cit., p. 138.
18. B. Latham, "On the Drainage of Fens", *Trans. Soc. of Eng.* (1862), p. 180.
19. L. Gibbs, op. cit., p. 280.
20. J. M. Heathcote, op. cit., p. 16.
21. L. Gibbs, op. cit., p. 277.
22. Collection of Letters belonging to J. M. Heathcote in the C.C.R.O.
23. W. H. Wheeler, op. cit., p. 78.
24. ibid., p. 108.
25. ibid., p. 107.
26. Waterbeach Level Order Book, 12 June 1893 and 1 October 1895.
27. J. P. Martin, *Presentation to Joseph Martin Esq., of Littleport, 1909.*
28. W. H. Wheeler, op. cit., pp. 106 ff.
29. C. A. Gill, "The Drainage of the Fen Districts". *Jour. of Munic. and County Eng.*, no. 9 (February 1915), p. 7.
30. L. Gibbs, op. cit., p. 281.
31. Waterbeach Level Order Book, 7 November 1908.
32. ibid., 5 October 1909.
33. Stretham Engine Records, Letter, 7 February 1921.
34. ibid., Letter, 17 April 1924.
35. ibid., Log Book, 20 February 1925.

Appendix I

Letter from James Watt to Towers Allen Esq., 5 December 1782.

Your obliging letter of the 3rd. instant to my partner Mr. Boulton, I take the liberty of answering in his absence.

You ask what quantity of water can be raised by a fire engine. The question does not admit of a definite answer the quantity being unlimited except by the impracticability or difficulty of executing pumps and cylinders large enough – The largest pump which I would advise the making of, in your case, would be six feet diameter, which pump with an 8 feet stroke should by calculation deliver each stroke 225 cubic feet, but pumps generally fall short of the effect calculated – I deduct the 25 feet and if it be kept in tolerable order, thinks myself safe in saying that it would actually raise 200 cubic feet of water pr. stroke, and as the engine would make 10 strokes pr. minute the pump would deliver 2000 cubic feet pr. minute.

You require the water to be raised 10 feet, to which adding 1 foot for what the water would sink below level in the canal from which it was suckit, and rise above level at the top of the pump, during the time of the stroke, the actual height of the column of water to be raised by the engine would be 11 feet – to raise such a column of water would, at least require a Cylinder of 48 inches in diam., but I would advise you to have one of 52 inches which by proper management will raise that quantity of water with rather less fuel than the other and will work easier and more nimbly.

As we never undertake the erection of Engines for a fixt sum and their expense is so much varied by local circumstance, I cannot pretend to determine *exactly* what would be the cost of such an engine; But in as far as our experience has shown us, the expense, in a general way, would be about £2500 – inclusive of the House, Boiler and pumps, but exclusive of any extra expense which may be incurred in making good a bad foundation, and in conveying the water to or from the engine. In cases where the height the water is to be raised is small, as in that you mention, the expense would probably be rather less than what I have mentioned, but the difference ought not to be reckoned upon as a saving; Estimates ought to be full.

Such an engine raising that quantity of water p. Stroke and working at the rate of 10 strokes pr. minute, will consume from $3\frac{1}{2}$ to 4 bushels of good Newcastle coals pr. hour.

In engines of smaller, or larger sizes, the expense of erection and the consumption of fuel will be pretty nearly proportioned to the quantities of water required to be raised, multiplied by the height to which it is to be raised; but larger Engines burn rather fewer coals in proportion and cost rather less money in proportion to their powers than smaller ones do; but the difference is not sufficiently defined to be reckoned upon.

Our terms are as follows –

1   The engine materials and every other expense attending the erection to be defrayed by our Employer.

2   We furnish all sorts of drawings and directions in writing which are necessary for the erection of the Engine without making any charge for the same.

3   We provide at the charge of our Employers, all such sorts of materials, as can not conveniently be provided by them or had in the neighbourhood – and we also provide

proper workmen or engineers to superintend and asist in the erection, such workmen being paid by our employers.

4   In place of profits we ask one third part of the savings of fuel made by our engine when compared with a common engine of equal power and working under similar circumstances – Formerly these comparative savings used to be determined by trial but as it was frequently impossible to find common engines in the neighbourhood which used the same sort of coals and were otherwise in similar circumstances, and as these trials were always attended with much loss of time and expense to both parties and frequently gave rise to disagreeable altercations and disputes we resolved to lay them entirely aside and as it appeared by the many trials which had been made that our engines produced from 3 to 4 times the effect from the same quantity of coals that the common ones did, we agreed to rate our engines as producing only 3 times the effect produced by the common ones, which terms have hitherto proved agreeable to our customers.

In your case in order to avoid any dispute we will agree to rate the common engine equal in power to the one I have calculated, as consuming 3 times $3\frac{1}{2}$ bushels or $10\frac{1}{2}$ bushels per hour, from which deducting $3\frac{1}{2}$ bushels the supposed consumption of our engine, there remains 7 bushels the total savings which being divided by 3 gives 2 1/3 bushels pr. hour or p. 600 strokes for our part of the savings or 3 883/1000 bushels per 1000 strokes or 38 8/10 bushels for every 10,000 strokes which the engine shall make (that is the price or value of so many coals, as they shall cost; and in order to keep account of the strokes actually made, we place or fix upon the working beam of the engine a machine called a counter, which unceasingly numbers the strokes, something in the way of a waywiser or Redometre and thus all parties may be satisfied, this counter is kept locked up under our key and our employers if they choose it may have another under their own key to which we can have no access.

As accidental circumstances frequently occasion Engines to burn more coals than was expected, we can not guarantee that such an engine will consume as little as 2 1/3 bushels p. hour, though it is our opinion that quantity ought to suffice, but will guarantee that it shall not require more than 4 bushels per hour when going ten strokes pr. minute, so if it should not do so upon trial, and we should not be able to help it, we will allow one third part of all it burns more than 4 bushels p. hour to be deducted from our premium.

5   The number of strokes made by the engine, to be taken once in 3 months and our premium to be paid us quarterly.

These are the principal articles of our agreements but in order to show them more clearly I have send with this a copy of the agreements we make in those cases, in law form, and have filled it up for an engine of the size calculated upon, if any other size is necessary, an agreement may be filled up suitable for it.

As I am entirely ignorant in what kind of situation the engine is wanted to be erected, what quantity of water is wanted to be raised, and, in what time, I have calculated at random; but shall be obliged to you to furnish me with these and any other facts you judge necessary, when it proves convenient.

I should have complied with your request and sent a drawing of the engine, but to make such a set of drawings and explanations as would be perfectly intellegable to gentlemen unaquainted with Fire engines would require a months labour of a good draughtsman and after all could not answer much good purpose, as in the general appearance our engines resemble the common ones and we take upon us to guarantee their performance.

Hoping that this proposal will meet your approbation

I am Sir

Your most respectful and most humble servant

James Watt.

Appendix II

Dimensions and details of steam-engines erected in the Fens between 1817 and 1835.

Sutton St Edmund. Grid Reference Sheet 124, 378144.
Erected *c*. 1817, scrapped *c*. 1834.
12 h.p.   Drained 4,000 acres.

Littleport and Downham, Ten Mile Bank Engine. Sheet 135, 601964.
.Erected 1819, scrapped 1842.
30 h.p.   Drained *c*. 10,000 acres.
Makers, Hague and Topham of London. Cost, Engine only, £1,800. Total about £6,000.
2 scoopwheels, 26′ diam., 2′ broad. Revs., 6 r.p.m.

Borough Fen. Sheet 124, 260081.
Erected 1820, scrapped *c*. 1834.
30 h.p.   Drained 6,000 acres.
Makers, possibly from Leeds. Cost, Engine only, ? £2,500.

Swaffham and Bottisham, Upware Engine. Sheet 135, 538698.
Erected 1821, scrapped 1939.
24 h.p.   Drained 5,800 acres.
Makers, Boulton and Watt, Birmingham. Cost, Engine and Boiler, £1,252. Total about
   £6,300.
Cylinder, $26\frac{1}{2}'' \times 60''$. Speed of engine, $21\frac{1}{2}$ r.p.m.
Scoopwheel, 26′ diam., 40 floats or ladles. Speed of scoopwheel, 5 r.p.m.

Deeping Fen, Two Engines at Pode Hole. Sheet 123, 214221.
Erected 1825, ceased working 1925, and preserved until 1952.
Drained 30,000 acres. Cost together about £17,000.

60 h.p. engine, *Kesteven*.
   Makers, Fenton and Murray, Leeds.
   Cylinder, $45'' \times 78''$.
   Beam, between centres, 20′ 6″.
   Connecting-rod, 20′ 6″.
   Flywheel, 24′ 6″, 6 spokes and segments.
   Scoopwheel (probably enlarged), 31′ diam., 5′ wide, 5′ 6″ dip.
   Rebuilt in 1881 by Watt and Company with piston valves.
   Gear ratio, $4\frac{1}{2}$ of scoopwheel to 22 of engine.

80 h.p. engine, *Holland*.
   Makers, Butterley Company.
   Cylinder, $44'' \times 96''$.

157

Beam, 2 cast-iron plates, 11½″ apart, 26′ 2″ long, 24′ 9″ between centres, 3′ 8″ deep at centre bearing.

Connecting-rod, 24′ 8″ between centres.

Flywheel, 24′ diam., 8 spokes, hexagonal boss. Rim section 12″ square, made of 3 sections, laminated round periphery. Approx. weight 21¼ tons.

Speed of engine, 16½ r.p.m., gearing 3½–1.

External drive, teeth 5¼″ × 15″ wide.

Scoopwheel, originally 28′ diam., width 5′, dip 5′, lifting 160 tons per minute. Later increased to 31′ diam., 40 scoops, 6′ 6″ long × 5′ wide.

March West Fen. Sheet 135, 381964.
Erected 1826, scrapped before 1900.
40 h.p.   Drained 3,600 acres.
Makers, Butterley Company.
Figures given in 1887:
Scoopwheel, 28′ diam., width of ladle, 2′ 9″, discharge, 70 tons per minute.
Coal consumed in 24 hours, 1 ton 17 cwt.

Pinchbeck South Fen or *Deeping Fen Fourth District.* Sheet 123, 215224.
Erected 1829, scrapped after 1900.
20 h.p.   Drained 3,000 acres. Cost £3,000.
Figures given in 1896:
Scoopwheel, 20′ diam., 42 scoops, 5′ 6″ long × 1′ 3″ wide.

Littleport and Downham, Hundred Foot Engine. Sheet 135, 508892.
Erected 1829, scrapped 1914.
Makers, Butterley Company. Cost about £7,500.
Cylinder, 42″ × 96″. 13 r.p.m.
Flywheel, 30′ diam., 8 spokes, 25–30 tons weight.
First scoopwheel, 2 speed, 35′ diam., 3′ 4″ wide, 5′ dip. New scoopwheel in 1881, 50′ diam., 3′ 4″ wide, 6′ dip, 60 ladles, weight 75 tons.
Piston valves added in 1882.

Middle Fen, Prickwillow. Sheet 135, 598825.
Erected 1832, turbine-pump with another engine added in 1880, but old engine kept as stand-by till scrapped in 1897.
60 h.p.   Drained 7,000 acres.
Makers, Butterley Company, Marine type, side-lever engine.
Scoopwheel, later 33′ 6″ diam., 2′ 1″ wide.

Waterbeach Level, Stretham Engine. Sheet 135, 517730.
Erected 1831, ceased regular work 1925, last ran 1941, but now preserved by the Stretham Engine Trust.
60 h.p.   Drained 5,600 acres.
Makers, Butterley Company. Cost £4,950.
Cylinder, 39″ × 96″.
Beam, 25′ centres, 2 cast-iron plates 10″ apart.
Connecting-rod, 21′.
Flywheel, 24′ diam., 8 spokes.

Scoopwheel, original wheel enlarged by extending the starts to 33′ 6″ in 1850, and width of ladles decreased from 3′ to 2′ 6″. In 1896 the wheel was completely rebuilt and the diam. increased to 37′ 6″.
Piston valves with variable cut-off were added in 1909.

Waldersea. Sheet 124, 433063.
Erected 1832, superseded 1833, and finally scrapped 1899.
60 h.p.　　Drained 6,500 acres.
Cornish engine with bucket-pump. Cost £3,000.
Cylinder, 40″ × 96″.
Bucket-pump, 72″ × 90″, lifting about 63 tons per minute.

Pinchbeck, Spalding Marsh. Sheet 123, 262262.
Erected 1833, ceased working in 1952, but now preserved.
20 h.p.　　"A" frame engine draining 4,000 acres.
Cylinder, 35″ × 54″.
Flywheel, 19′ 6″ diam., 6 spokes, 5 tons weight.
Beam, 13′.
Scoopwheel, 22′ diam., 40 ladles, 2′ 3″ wide, 4′ dip. Gearing 4·46–1, engine speed 30 r.p.m., scoopwheel $6\frac{3}{4}$′.
Later fitted with Worthington-Simplex piston valve.

Magdalen Fen. Sheet 124, 598098.
Erected 1834, scrapped *c.* 1914.
40 h.p.　　Drained 4,000 acres.
Makers, Butterley Company.
When this engine had its cylinder rebored many years ago in King's Lynn, the time for each cut is reputed to have been 10 hours.

Binnimore, or *March First.* Sheet 135, 433977.
Erected 1633, scrapped 1933.
30 h.p.　　Drained 3,000 acres.
Makers, Butterley Company.
Cylinder, 30″ × 72″.
1 boiler, 7′ diam. × 27′ long.
Scoopwheel, 34′ diam.

Dimensions and details of steam-engines erected in the Fens between 1835 and 1852. This list is probably not complete.

Blankney, Linwood and Martin.
Erected *c.* 1834–5.
30 h.p., on Martin Delph.

Nocton, Potterhamworth and Branston.
Erected 1834–5.
40 h.p.　　Drained 5,600 acres.
Beam-engine.
Scoopwheel, 3′ wide, ladles, 6′ long.

Feltwell, Brandon Engine.
Erected 1836, scrapped before 1880.
20 h.p.
Makers, Butterley Company.

Soham Mere. Sheet 135, 571748.
Erected 1836, scrapped 1910.
40 h.p.   Drained 1,600 acres plus 400 of highland, but it had a large lift.
Makers, Butterley Company.
Scoopwheel, 36′ diam.

Over Fen.
Erected 1837, scrapped 1937.
20 h.p.   Drained 1,600 acres.
Makers, J. Clark and Company, Deptford.
Cylinder, $13\frac{1}{2}'' \times 39''$, "D" type slide valve.
Flywheel, 14′ diam., 6 spokes.
Speed of engine, 33 r.p.m., gearing 4–1.
Scoopwheel, 16′ diam., 32 ladles, 4′ 6″ long × 15″ wide.

Timberland.
Erected 1839, scrapped 1881, when a new engine and centrifugal pump replaced a beam-
    engine and scoopwheel, which was of insufficient power.

Mepal. Sheet 135, 441822.
Erected 1840, scrapped *c.* 1926.
80 h.p.   Drained 10,348 acres.
Makers, Butterley Company.
Scoopwheel, 32′ diam. but by 1884 36′ diam., width 4′, making $3\frac{1}{2}$ r.p.m., discharging
    120 tons per minute.

Chettisham, Ely.
Erected 1841.
Grasshopper type.

Billinghay South District, Chapel Hill Engine.
Erected 1841, scrapped 1935.
30 h.p.   Drained 4,500 acres.
Makers, Green Atkinson and Company, Phoenix Works, Wakefield. Cost £3,600.
Cylinder, 31″ × 78″.
Flywheel, 21′ 6″ diam., 8 spokes.
Scoopwheel, 27′ diam., 42 floats, 6′ long × 2′ 3″ wide.

Burnt Fen, Lark Engine. Sheet 135, 600826.
Erected 1842, possibly replaced in 1883 by horizontal engine.
40 h.p.   Side-lever engine.
Makers, Butterley Company.
Scoopwheel, 34′ 4″ diam. × 2′ wide.

160

Chear Fen Engine. Sheet 135, 497718.
Erected 1842, scrapped after 1936.
Makers, I. Clark and Company, Sutherland.
Cylinder, $30'' \times 60''$.
Beam centres, 20' 3".
Flywheel, 20' diam. with 8 spokes and rim in 8 segments.
Scoopwheel, 28' diam., 40 paddles, 5' 6" long $\times$ 1' 8" wide.
Engine revolutions, 18 r.p.m., 5–1 reduction gear to wheel.

Littleport and Downham, Ten Mile Bank Engine. Sheet 135, 601964.
Replaced old engine in 1842, scrapped 1912.
80 h.p.   With Hundred Foot engine, drained 35,000 acres.
Makers, engine by Butterley Company, engine-house by Goose and Dyson. Cost £7,100.,
Scoopwheel, originally 42' diam., increased in 1879 to 43' 8" $\times$ 36" wide; 50 scoops, 7' 6"
   long, discharge, 213 tons per minute, mean lift, 11'.
In 1883, 3 Lancashire boilers, 24' long $\times$ 7' diam.

Smithey Fen. Sheet 135, 448719.
Erected 1842, scrapped after 1936.
Makers, J. Clarke and Company, Sunderland, builders, Bennet and Son.
Cylinder, $32\frac{1}{2}'' \times 64''$.
Scoopwheel, 28' diam.

Southery.
Erected 1842.
Beam-engine and scoopwheel.

Bourne North Fen, at Gutheram Cote. Sheet 123, 173225.
Erected 1845.
30 h.p.
Makers, Butterley Company.
Cylinder, $45'' \times 72''$.
Scoopwheel, 15' diam., 4' 3" wide, 30 scoops, 3' 10" long.
Engine revs., 19–$4\frac{1}{2}$ of wheel.

Mildenhall. Sheet 135, 623801.
Erected 1844.
Beam-engine and scoopwheel.

Hilgay, Stocks Farm.
Erected 1845.
Beam-engine and scoopwheel.

Bardney, Stixwould.
Erected 1846.
30 h.p.   Drained 2,610 acres.
Cost £3,545.
Cylinder, $32'' \times 72''$.
Scoopwheel, 28' diam. $\times$ 2' 4" wide, 40 scoops, 5' 6" long.
Engine revs., 16–6 of wheel, lift, 4'.

Benwick, White Fen Engine.
Erected 1847, scrapped after 1936.
Makers, Butterley Company.   Drained 2,400 acres.
Cylinder, 30″ × 36″.
Beam centres, 9′ 6″, made from 2 cast-iron plates.
Flywheel, 15′ 4″ diam., 6 spokes.
Scoopwheel, 28′ 6″ diam., 20″ wide, ladles, 5′ 9″ long.
Engine, 36 r.p.m., 8–1 internal reduction gear.

Fordham.
Erected 1847.
Makers, Overton and Wilson, Hull.
Cylinder, 21″ × 48″.
Beam centres, 11′.
Flywheel, 18′ diam., 6 spokes and segments.
Scoopwheel, 28′ diam. × 15″ wide.
2 boilers.

Hilgay, Martin's Farm.
Erected 1847.
Beam-engine and scoopwheel.

Burnt Fen, Brandon.
Erected 1848.
Beam-engine and scoopwheel.

Tilney St Lawrence, Marshland.
Erected 1849.
Beam-engine and scoopwheel.

Whittlesey Mere, Holme Fen. Sheet 134, 238904.
Erected 1852, scrapped 1877, and replaced by a larger engine.
25 h.p.
Makers, Easton and Amos.
Beam-engine and horizontal centrifugal pump.
Original lift, 4–5′, but increased to 9′.

Appendix III

Estimate for the Swaffham and Bottisham Engine-house, for those parts above ground.
(J. Rennie, Letter Books, vol. 11, 9 November 1820.)

65 Rods of Brickwork,	@	£16.	£1040. 0. 0.
146 feet of Stone,	@	5/-	36. 10. 0.
1591 feet of Timber for Roof, Doors, Floors and Windows,	@	5/-	397. 15. 0.
30 Yards superl. of cistern lined with cement,	@	2/6	3. 15. 0.
23¾ Squares of Pantiling,	@	48/-	57. 0. 0.
146¾ yards of plastering – 2 coats of lime and hair,	@	1/10	13. 9. 0.
39¼ yards of 2 coat ceiling, laths and nails,	@	2/6	4. 18. 1.
28¾ yards of Brick Floor,	@	3/-	4. 6. 3.
3.1.23 Milled Lead for Gutters and Roof,	@	34/-	5. 17. 5.
90 feet of glazing and painting sashes,	@	3/6	15. 5. 0.
66 feet of Common glass Windows,	@	1/8	5. 10. 10.
19½ yards of Yorkshire flag and Setting,	@	27/-	6. 16. 6.
526 lbs. of iron work,	@	6d.	13. 4. 0.
80 feet of Timber in the Well and Beams	@	3/9	15. 0. 0.
90 floors of excavation,	@	7/-	34. 13. 0.
486 feet timbers in Foundations,	@	4/-	92. 4. 0.
27 Rods of extra Brickwork in Foundations,	@	£16.	432. 0. 0.
Sinking of Well, clearing away water and sundry expenses,			110. 0. 0.
			£2288. 4. 1.

Estimate of Expense for Sundry Materials and Labour wanted for fixing the wheels at the intended New Engine-house in Swaffham Fen, according to Plans and Specification.

Sundry Brickwork, 20½ Rods,	@	£14. 14. 0	£301. 7. 0.
Sundry Stone Work, 4806 Cubic Feet,	@	4/9	1141. 8. 6.
Cutting Foundation and Pumping Water,			20. 0. 0.
			£1462. 15. 6.

163

Appendix IV

Early Boulton and Watt steam-engines sent to Holland.

1785   Batavian Society, Hoogendyk, Rotterdam, Holland, to drain the polder of Blydorp and Kool.
Cylinder, $34'' \times 6'$ $0''$, Pump $55'' \times 6'$ $0''$. Equal beam and chain, N.H.P. 22·3.

1790   Mydrechtsche, called M.D.T. Engine. Engine erected at Mydrechtsche Polder or Mere, by the River Amstel in the province of South Holland in the Netherlands, near Withoorm states of Utrecht.
Cylinder, $48'' \times 8'$ $0''$, Pump, $48'' \times 8'$ $0''$, Equal beam and chain, N.H.P. 49·1. 10 strokes per minute, Lift 18 feet, engine sent in 1792 and erected in 1794.

1801   Hellevoetsluis, Cylinder $30\frac{3}{4}'' \times 6'$, Double acting, N.H.P. 30·2.

1803   J. D. Huichelbos Van Leinder. Steam engine in Ontlast Sluis, by the River Yssel, erected in the Krimpenrewaard, in 1803–1804 under the direction of A. Blanken Jann Holland, to lift 575 cubic feet 3 to 7 feet high, 20 strokes per minute.
Cylinder, $31\frac{1}{2}'' \times 2'$ $6''$, Pump, $48'' \times 2'$ $6''$, Equal beam and Parallel Motion, N.H.P. 14·3.

1806   Katwyk and Rhine Canal, Katwyk on Lee, Holland.
Cylinder, $36'' \times 3'$ $6''$, pump $54'' \times 3'$ $6''$, lift $7\frac{1}{2}''$, $17\frac{1}{2}$ strokes per minute, equal beam to raise 877 cubic ft.

1822   Nieive Deep, Holland, with nine pumps.
Cylinder, $36'' \times 6'$ $0''$, Equal beam, parallel motion, but with two other beams so each beam worked three pumps. Diameter of Pumps, $23''$, $23\frac{1}{4}''$, $23\frac{1}{2}''$, $23\frac{1}{4}''$, $23''$, $23''$, $33''$, $32\frac{1}{4}''$, $32\frac{3}{4}''$. N.H.P. 25.

Appendix V

Deeping Fen Engines—*water lifted each month*

Month	Rain ins.	80 Horse lifted tons	60 Horse lifted tons	Rain ins.	80 Horse lifted tons	60 Horse lifted tons	
1830				**1831**			
May	4·7	1,638,660		1·25	156,420		
June	4·63	3,004,640	181,440	3·1	114,820	10,500	
July	3·2	1,456,570	133,920	4·9		597,040	
Aug.	2·12	23,160		4·1	276,960	500,845	
Sept.	4·79	1,675,920		4·25	641,200	81,700	
Oct.	0·63	952,500	150,060	2·9	3,120,760	1,427,552	
Nov.	1·87	670,320	879,840	2·5	2,546,800	1,189,890	
Dec.	1·3	2,741,580	330,540	2·4	3,623,690	1,787,880	
1831				**1832**			
Jan.	2·0	2,916,680	474,650	1·25	1,855,120	2,337,645	
Feb.	3·0	5,669,640	2,293,820	0·1	324,200	434,700	
March	1·62	2,623,500		2·8	1,765,260	913,695	
April	2·32	488,200		2·5	715,920		
Total	32·16	23,861,370	4,444,270	32·05	15,141,150	9,281,447	
1832				**1833**			
May	3·1	1,377,400	347,980	0·82	169,040		
June	3·1	910,180		3·12	380,620	2,500	
July	2·3	27,135		0·3		49,100	
Aug.	4·25	74,925		3·5	12,780	18,020	
Sept.	0·37	21,735	15,309	1·2	159,840	96,480	
Oct.	3·1	348,685		2·1	394,560	200,480	
Nov.	3·5	1,724,480	1,135,120	0·75	380,990	124,020	
Dec.	2·5	3,410,260	2,018,235	1·7	687,740	70,280	
1833				**1834**			
Jan.	1·25	2,213,640	1,394,625	2·25	1,616,530	994,305	
Feb.	5·15	5,594,980	3,859,425	0·5	473,460	454,060	
March	2·06	2,703,300	1,313,840	0·5	125,700	81,300	
April	3·0	2,452,220	1,599,380	1·0	8,940	5,850	
Total	33·68	20,858,940	11,683,914	17·74	4,410,200	2,096,395	
1834				**1835**			
May	0·5	9,320	6,420	2·0	781,080	420,380	Jan.
June	0·9	6,900	4,540	1·75	469,120	335,330	Feb.
July	6·25	72,240		2·5	2,093,470	1,365,710	March
Aug.	2·1	67,920		1·5	521,130	329,090	April
Sept.	1·25		46,080	21·60	4,068,590	2,565,150	Total
Oct.	1·0	18,640	40,320				
Nov.	1·25	18,570	11,060				
Dec.	0·6	10,200	6,220				

Appendix VI

Waterbeach Level—*expenses of running Stretham Engine*

YEAR	Rainfall to end of April ins.	Hours worked by Steam Engine from April to April hours	mins.	Tons of Coal Consumed tons	cwts.	Tons of Coal purchased in Year tons	cwts.	Cost of Coal purchased in Year £	s.	d.	Total cost of working Engine including Coal £	s.	d.	Average Cost per Acre s.	d.
1854	20·12	752	—	not known		389	—	356	14	2	411	11	9	1	8
1881	23·69	1744	—	429	—	369	3	292	17	1	396	1	8	1	7
1882	25·27	978	30	277	—	281	17	224	0	11	286	18	8	1	2
1883	25·08	1776	30	449	13	454	13	379	5	4	477	18	2	1	9
1884	21·09	1008	30	219	19	239	19	201	19	2	252	17	1	1	0
1885	17·69	302	—	75	—	233	3	195	5	3	270	8	6	1	1
1886	24·22	917	45	230	—	—	—	—	—	—	75	8	½		4
1887	23·38	754	—	227	—	232	—	173	0	8	204	4	9		10
1888	15·34	69	15	25	—	253	19	165	3	4	255	16	11	1	0
1889	21·08	228	45	90	—	—	—	—	—	—	90	8	10		4
1890	29·13	1201	—	280	—	205	18	154	14	4	196	18	5		9
1891	16·78	82	—	22	—	207	7	178	16	10	180	0	6		9
1892	30·08	1062	—	246	—	116	1	99	12	2	129	6	10		6
1893	25·83	1410	—	358	—	253	13	235	0	8	338	17	10	1	4
1894	21·49	394	30	100	—	102	18	81	0	10	206	7	6		10
1895	22·31	948	—	224	—	276	9	232	17	11	359	6	7	1	5
1896	17·71	474	30	128	—	128	8	100	0	11	133	9	8		6
1897	22·12	1420	—	302	—	258	9	192	18	2	265	15	6	1	1
1898	13·47	62	15	20	—	103	—	81	18	11	170	9	6		8
1899	18·84	235	—	67	—	107	7	88	19	8	106	18	11		5
1900	18·22	896	15	195	—	65	—	85	15	4	164	14	11		8

The average rainfall from 1839 to 1925 was **21·21 ins.**
The average number of hours which the engine worked each year from 1839 to 1925 was **769 hours**

Appendix VII

House of Commons, Accounts and Papers

Average price of all sorts of grain

(From 1821, vol. 17, p. 11)

Year	Wheat	Oats	Year	Wheat	Oats
1791	47·2	17·7	1815	64·4	23·10
92	42·11	17·10	16	75·10	23·6
93	48·11	21·3	17	94·9	32·1
94	51·8	22·0	18	84·1	32·11
1795	74·2	24·9	19	73·0	29·4
96	77·1	21·9	1820	65·7	24·4
97	53·1	16·9	(From 1833, vol. 5, p. 635)		
98	50·3	19·10	1821	54·5	18·11
99	67·6	27·7	22	43·3	17·7
1800	113·7	39·10	23	51·9	30·7
01	118·3	36·6	24	62·0	24·1
02	67·5	20·7	1825	66·6	24·11
03	56·6	21·2	26	56·11	25·11
04	60·1	23·9	27	56·9	27·4
1805	67·10	28·0	28	60·5	22·0
06	79·0	25·8	29	66·3	22·9
07	73·3	28·1	1830	64·3	24·5
08	79·0	33·8	31	66·4	25·4
09	95·7	32·8	32	58·8	20·5
1810	106·2	29·4	(From 1836, vol. 8, p. 217)		
11	94·6	27·11	33	52·11	18·5
12	125·5	44·0	34	46·2	20·11
13	108·9	39·5	1835	39·4	22·0
14	73·11	26·6			

Appendix VIII

Figures given by Dempsey to show the temperature and evaporation rates during the year (*c.* 1852).

Month	Highest	Thermometer Lowest	Mean	Month	Evaporation per cent	Remainder per cent
January	52·0	11·0	36·1	January	29·3	70·7
February	53·0	21·0	38·0	February	21·6	78·4
March	66·0	24·0	43·9	March	33·4	66·6
April	74·0	29·0	49·9	April	79·0	21·0
May	70·0	33·0	54·0	May	94·2	5·8
June	90·0	37·0	58·7	June	98·3	1·7
July	76·0	42·0	61·0	July	98·2	1·8
August	82·0	41·0	61·6	August	98·6	1·4
September	76·0	36·0	57·8	September	80·1	18·9
October	68·0	27·0	48·9	October	50·5	49·9
November	62·0	23·0	42·9	November	15·1	84·9
December	55·0	17·0	39·3	December	0·0	100·0
				Mean	57·6	42·4

Appendix IX

Figures of evaporation rates from the Rijnland Drainage Board, Holland, in 1962.

Month	R	Eo	f	Ep	Ep—R
January	88	7	0·6	4	—84
February	49	25	0·6	15	—34
March	40	34	0·7	24	—16
April	60	66	0·7	46	—14
May	82	81	0·8	65	—17
June	14	123	0·8	98	+84
July	86	107	0·8	86	+ 0
August	79	108	0·8	86	+ 7
September	104	73	0·7	51	—53
October	77	36	0·7	25	—52
November	54	14	0·6	8	—46
December	93	7	0·6	4	—89
Total	826	681		512	

R=Rainfall at Oude-Wetering per month measured in millimetres.

Eo=Evaporation of an open surface of water according to the calculations of Penman, calculated as averages from details of the Meteorological Institute with regards to the evaporation in the Bilt and Den Helder.

f=Correcting factor according to Penman in order to calculate Eo into Ep.

Ep=Evaporation from soil and vegetable growth with good water supply (potential evaporation or transpiration) per month.

$Ep-R$=Shortage of rain (+) or surplus of rain (—) per month: (—) to be pumped out, (+) to be let in.

Appendix X

Notes on various old-fashioned measures

Horse-power, Smeaton made one horse-power equal five men, French writers, six or seven men, Telford thought it equal to five or six.[1]

Windmills with four sails, measuring 66 French feet from one extremity to the other, and 6 feet wide, raise 1,000 lbs. 218 feet in one minute, and if working on an average of 8 hours per day, is equal to 34 men; as it has been estimated that 25 square feet of canvas perform the daily work of a man.[2]

On measuring a bushel . . . rarely practised, except for those coals which are transported by sea, which are in consequence chargeable with a duty (hundred weight=112 lbs., ton, 2,240 lbs.).

The legal coal bushel may, therefore, be stated to contain 2,815 cubic inches or 1·63 cubic feet. 3 bushels of coal are put into a sack and 12 such sacks (=36 busels) make a chaldron.

The weight of coals varies considerably in the different sorts, but the chaldron (=36 bushels) is usually reckoned to weigh 27 hundred weight ($\times$112)=3,024 lbs. which is at the rate of $\frac{3}{4}$ of a cwt. (or 84 lbs.) per bushel. This number has been adopted in the present work, because it is the actual weight of the best qualities of the Newcastle coals, though inferior sorts are not above 78 or 80 lbs. per bushel.[3]

NOTES

1. T. Telford, *Life of Thomas Telford . . .* (1838), p. 671.
2. ibid.
3. J. Farey, *A Treatise on the Steam Engine* (1827), p. 337.

Appendix XI

Bibliography

Acts of Parliament

mentioned in the text.

23 Hen. VIII, c. 5	General Drainage Act
43 Eliz. I, c. 11	General Drainage Act
Pretended Act, 29 May 1649	Bedford Level
15 Char. II, c. 17	Bedford Level
16 & 17 Char. II, c. 11, 22 Char. II, c. 15	Acts for Deeping Fen
13 Geo. I, c. 18	Haddenham Level
11 Geo. II, c. 34	Cawdle Fen
11 Geo. II, c. 39	Deeping Fen
14 Geo. II, c. 24	Waterbeach Level
27 Geo. III, c. 2	Borough Fen
29 Geo. III, c. 22	Middle Fen, Ely
30 Geo. III, c. 74	Waterbeach Level
34 Geo. III, c. 92	Wisbech Canal
34 Geo. III, c. 102	Welland River
37 Geo. III, c. 88	Waterbeach Level
39 & 40 Geo. III, c. 109	Horncastle Navigation
52 Geo. III, c. 143	Borough Fen
53 Geo. III, c. 81	Waterbeach Level
53 Geo. III, c. 107	Waterbeach Level
53 Geo. III, c. 161	Hatfield Chase
54 Geo. III, c. 168	London and Cambridge Junction Canal
57 Geo. III, c. 69	South Holland Drainage Act
59 Geo. III, c. 77	Borough Fen
59 Geo. III, c. 78	Swaffham and Bottisham District
4 Geo. IV, c. 76	Deeping Fen
8 Geo. IV, c. 85	Nene Outfall
9 Geo. IV, c. 40	March Fourth District
9 Geo. IV, c. 89	Waldersea District
10 Geo. IV, c. 104	Nene Outfall
11 Geo. IV, c. 53	North Level
1 Wil. IV, c. 27	North Level
1 & 2 Wil. IV, c. 6	Abolition of Coal Tax
2 Wil. IV, c. 95	Pinchbeck Fen

Manuscript Sources

The places where these were found are included for future reference.

Bedford Level Corporation (C.C.R.O.):
Records of Earlier Courts of Sewers relating to the Bedford Level Corporation.
London Order Books, beginning May 1663.
Conservators Proceedings, Ely, beginning 1665.
Bedford Level Corporation as Commissioners of Sewers.
Bedford Level Corporation Minute Books.

Boulton and Watt Collection, Birmingham Public Library.
  Various Letters from the elder and junior Watt.
  Letters to the firm from T. Allen, M. Boulton, J. Rennie, W. Swansborough, J. Walker, R. Wild.
  Engine Books for costs and details.
Deeping Fen (L.C.R.O.):
  Adventurers Minutes.
  Adventurers Accounts.
  General Drainage Trust, Minutes.
  General Joint Works, Drainage Trustees Minutes.
Ely Diocesan Records (C.U.L.):
  Various papers relating to fen drainage.
Haddenham Level:
  Account Books, 1739–41, and 1743–5, now kept among the Ely Diocesan Records.
Harleian Manuscripts (B.M.):
  701, Valores omnium maneriorum . . .
  702, Liber Curiarum manerii in Gedney.
  5011, A collection of papers about draining of Fens in several counties of England by Sir
    William Dugdale.
  6838, Nos. 37, 38, 39, 40, various papers relating to the Fens.
Lansdowne Manuscripts (B.M.):
  41, Nos. 45–56, concerning Carleton's disputes.
  44, No. 57, ibid.
  46, No. 56, ibid.
  51, Nos. 87, 88, ibid.
  60, No. 34, A Discourse of Humphrey Bradley (in Italian).
  87, No. 4, Distress in the Fenlands.
  110, Nos. 3–7, A Patent and Sir. Wm. Russell about Thorney.
Littleport and Downham District (Fen Office at Littleport):
  Order Books.
  Account Books.
John Rennie:
  Twelve Volumes of Letter Books, at the Institution of Civil Engineers.
State Papers (P.R.O.):
  Dom Eliz., 106, No. 62, Patent of Peter Morrice.
            127, No. 57, Patent of Tho. Goldinge.
            213, No. 28, Carleton.
            219, No. 73, ibid.
            244, No. 97, Petition of Humphrey Bradley.
            241, No. 114, Patent of Guillaume Mostart.
Waterbeach Level:
  Minute or Order Books, 1775–1839 and 1873–1910, at Archer and Archer, Ely.
  Account Book, 1813–84, Francis and Company, Cambridge.
  Contract for building the engine-house, dated 8.10.1830 (Articles of Agreement) at Archer
    and Archer, Ely.
  Various papers found in a chest at the Stretham Engine, containing:
    Engine Log Books, 1839–1941.
    Abstract of Accounts, 1879–1925.
    Petty Cash Accounts, 1845–1925.
Tycho Wing:
  Letter Books for when he was acting as Agent of the Duke of Bedford about 1820, at Thorney
    and the North Level Internal Drainage Board, Thorney.

Books

D'Acres, R. *The Art of Water Drawing*. London, Henry Brome, 1659.

Acts of Parliament, *see* separate list.

Acts of the Privy Council (P.R.O.).

Aikin, G. "Culture of the Cambridgeshire Fens", *Transactions of the Society of Arts*, vol. 52, 1838–9.

Airy, W. "Remarks on the Construction of the Course, and Design for a new and Improved Scoopwheel", *Engineering*, vol. IX, 1870.

Allen, T. *The History of the County of Lincoln*, London, John Saunders, 1833.

Almack, B. "On the Agriculture of Norfolk", *J.R.A.S.*, vol. 5, 1844.

Altes, J. K. *Sir Cornelius Vermuyden*. London, Williams and Norgate, 1925.

Anonymous
> *Observations on the means of better draining the Middle and South Levels of the Fens, by two gentlemen who have taken a view thereof.* 1777 (B.M.).
>
> *Remarks on the New Cut proposed to be made from Eau-Brink to Lynn, by an Inhabitant of Lynn.* 1793 (Fen Tracts, C.C.R.O.).
>
> *A Remonstrance against the Postscript to the Report of Mr. John Rennie concerning the Drainage of the East, West and Wildmore Fens.* 1800.
>
> *Committee on the Eau Brink Drainage, Wednesday, 11th. of March, 1818.*
>
> *Report of the Proceedings of the Committee for taking into consideration Mr. Rennie's Reports on the Improvement of the Outfall of the River Nene.* Wisbech, White and Leach, 1821.
>
> *Report on the Outfall of the River Nene*, August, 1821.
>
> *Lines addressed to the Commissioners of Burnt Fen by their Officer on his Thirtieth Anniversary in their service, Feb. 18, 1861.* Littleport, G. T. Watson.

Armstrong, J. *History of the Navigation of King's Lynn*. 1725 (C.U.L.).

Ashton, T. S., and Sykes, J. *Coal Industry of the Eighteenth Century*. Manchester University Press, 1929.

Astbury, A. K. *The Black Fens*. Cambridge, Golden Head Press, 1958.

Bacon, R. N. *The Report on the Agriculture of Norfolk*. London, Ridgways, Chapman and Hall, 1844.

Badeslade, T. *The History of the Ancient and Present State of the Navigation of the Port of King's Lyn, and of Cambridge, and the rest of the trading Towns in those parts: and of the navigable rivers that have their course through the Great-Level of the Fens. . . .* London, 1725.
> *A Scheme for draining the Great Level of the Fens called Bedford Level; and for improving the Navigation of Lyn-Regis; Founded upon Self-evident principles in Experimental Philosophy and Practical Mathematics and Historical Facts.* (Partly printed in Labelye, *Result of a View of the Great Level of the Fens . . .*), 1729.

Bateson, P. *Some Papers Relating to the General Draining of Marsh Land in the County of Norfolk, with Mr. Berner's Objections and Proposals.* 1710 (Fen Tracts, C.C.R.O.).

Blith, W. *The English Improver*. London, John Wright, 1st ed. 1649, 2nd ed. 1652.

Bloom, A. *The Fens*. London, W. Clowes and Sons, 1953.

Board of Agriculture
> *Report of Committee appointed by the Board to take into consideration the state of waste lands and common fields of this kingdom, Jan. 1795.*
>
> *Agricultural State of the Kingdom in February, March and April, 1816.*
>
> In their series, *The General View of the County of . . .*, the following have been consulted:

Gooch, W. *Cambridge*. 1806, 1811 and 1813.
Kent, N. *Norfolk*. 1794.
Maxwell, G. *Huntingdon*. 1793.
Parkinson, R. *Huntingdon*. 1813.
Stone, T. *Huntingdon*. 1793.
Stone, T. *Lincoln*. 1794.
Vancouver, C. *Cambridge*. 1794.
Young, A. *Lincoln*. 1799.
Young, A. *Norfolk*. 1804.

Boucher, C. T. G. *John Rennie, 1761–1821, The Life and Work of a Great Engineer.* Manchester University Press, 1963.

Bridgman, C. *An Answer to a Report of the Present State of the Great Level of the Fens.* 1724 (C.U.L.).

Burrell, A. *A Briefe Relation discovering Plainely the true Causes why the great Levell of the Fenns in the Severall Counties of Norfolk, Suffolk, Cambridge, Huntingdon, Northampton and Lincoln Shires have been drowned and made unfruitful for many years past.* London, Constable 1642 (B.M.).

    Exceptions against Sir Cornelius Virmudens Discourse for the Draining of the great Fennes. . . . London, Constable, 1642 (B.M.).

Caird, J. *English Agriculture in 1850–51.* London, Longman and Company, 1852.

Carter, E. *History of the County of Cambridge.* Cambridge, 1753.

Casaubon, I. *Ephemerides.* Ed. J. Russell, Oxford, 1850.

Clark, R. H. "Early Engines of the Eastern Counties", *English Mechanics,* 1936/7.

    Steam Engine Builders of Suffolk, Essex and Cambridgeshire. 1950.

Clarke, J. A. "The Great Level of the Fens", *J.R.A.S.,* vol. 8, 1847.

    "On the Farming of Lincolnshire", *J.R.A.S.,* vol. 12, 1851.

    Fen Sketches. London, 1852.

Clay, W. K. *History of the Parish of Waterbeach.* Cambridge, 1859.

Cobbett, W. *Rural Rides.* 1830.

Creassy, J. *The Report and Opinion of James Creassy respecting the Drainage of the Middle and South Levels of the Fenns.* 1777 (B.M.).

Cuppari, G. "On the Practical Results obtained from various Water-Raising Machines in Holland", *Transactions of the Institute of Civil Engineers,* vol. 75, 1883–4.

Darby, H. C. "Windmill Drainage in the Bedford Level", *The Engineer,* vol. 160, 1935.

    The Medieval Fenland. Cambridge, 1940.

    The Draining of the Fens. Cambridge, 1940.

Defoe, D. *A tour through the whole Island of Great Britain.* 1724.

Dempsey, G. D. *Rudimentary Treatise on the Drainage of Districts and Lands.* London, John Weale, 1854.

Denson, J. *Peasants Voice to Landowners, written by a self-taught inhabitant of Waterbeach.* 1820.

Dickinson, H. W. *A Short History of the Steam Engine.* Cambridge, 1938.

Dodson, W. *The Designe for the perfect draining of the Great Level of the Fens.* London, R. Wood, 1665 (B.M.).

Dugdale, Sir W. *The History of Imbanking and Drayning of divers Fenns and Marshes, both in foreign parts and in this Kingdom; and of the improvements thereby.* London, Alice Warren, 1662.

Dundonald, Earl of (A. Cochrane). *Treatise showing the intimate connection that exists between Agriculture and Chemistry.* London, 1795.

Elstobb, W. *Some Thoughts on Rosewell's and other Schemes for Draining the South and Middle Levels of the Fens.* 1742 (B.M.).

    The Pernicious consequences of replacing Denver Dam and Sluices etc., considered in a letter to Mr. John Leaford. 1745 (B.M.).

    Observations on an address to the public . . . superscribed Bedford Level and signed C. N. Cole. 1776 (B.M.).

    An Historical Account of the Great Level of The Fens, called Bedford Level, and other Fens, Marshes and low lands. 1793 (B.M.).

Ennion, E. A. R. *Cambridgeshire, Huntingdonshire and the Isle of Ely.* London, R. Hale, 1951.

    Adventurers Fen. London, Methuen, 1942.

Farey, J. *A Treatise on the Steam Engine.* London, Longmans, 1827.

Forbes, R. J. *Studies in Ancient Technology.* Leiden, E. J. Brill, 1955.

Fowler, G. "Shrinkage of the Peat Covered Fenlands", *Geog. Soc. Journal,* vol. 81, 1933.

Gibbs, L. "Pumping Machinery in the Fenland and by the Trent-side", *Minutes of the Proceedings of the Institution of Civil Engineers*, vol. XCIV, 1888.

Gilbert, Davies. "Paper to the Royal Society on Steam Engines", *Philosophical Transactions*, March 1830.

Gill, C. A. "The Drainage of the Fen District", *Journal of Municipal and County Engineers*, no. 9, February 1915.

Glynn, J. "Draining Land by Steam Power", *Transactions of the Society of Arts*, vol. 51, 1838.

Golborne, J. *The Report of James Golborne of the City of Ely, Engineer*, 1791 (Fen Tracts, C.C.R.O.).

Gooch, W. *See* Board of Agriculture.

Gunning, H. *Reminiscences of the University, Town and County of Cambridge from the year 1780.* London, George Bell, 1854.

Hadfield, C. *British Canals.* London, Phoenix, 1950.

Hammond, J. L. and B. *The Village Labourer.* London, Longmans, 1911.

Hardwicke, Earl of. *Observations upon the Eau-Brink Cut, with a proposal offered to the Consideration of the Friends of the Drainage. c.* 1793 (Fen Tracts, C.C.R.O.).

Harris, L. E. *Vermuyden and the Fens.* London, Cleaver-Hume Press, 1953.
The Two Netherlanders. Cambridge, Heffer, 1961.

Hartlib, S. *A Discourse of Husbandry used in Brabant and Flanders.* London, 1651.

Heathcote, Sir G. *Thoughts of a Lincolnshire Freeholder on the address of Sir G. Heathcote.* London, 1794 (B.M.).

Heathcote, J. M. Collection of Letters in the C.C.R.O.
Reminiscences of Fen and Mere. London, 1876.
Scoopwheel and Centrifugal Pump. London, 1877.

Hillen, N. *History of King's Lynn.* Norwich, 1907.

Hodskinson, J. *The Report of Joseph Hodskinson, Engineer, on the probable effect which a New Cut now in Contemplation from Eau Brink to a little above Lynn will have on the harbour and navigation of Lynn.* 1793 (Fen Tracts, C.C.R.O.).

House of Commons: Journals
Minutes of Evidence before Select Committee on Petitions complaining of the Depressed State of Agriculture, April 1821.
Minutes of Evidence Taken before Select Committee on Agricultural Distress, March 1836.

Johnson, C. W. "On the Improvement of Peat Soils", *J.R.A.S.*, vol. 2, 1841.

Jonas, S. "On the Farming of Cambridgeshire", *J.R.A.S.*, vol. 7, 1846.

Kent, N. *See* Board of Agriculture.

Kinderley, N. *The Ancient and Present State of the Navigation of the Towns of Lyn, Wisbech, Spalding and Boston.* London, 1751 (B.M.).

Kirkus, M. *The Records of the Commissioners of Sewers in the Parts of Holland, 1547–1603.* (Lincoln Record Society.) Lincoln, Ruddock and Sons, 1959.

Labelye, C. *Result of a View of the Great Level of the Fens, taken in July 1745.* London, 1745.

Lambert, J. M. *The Making of the Broads*, R.G.S. Series (1960).

Latham, B. "On the Drainage of the Fens", *Transactions of the Society of Engineers*, 1862.

Leaford, J. *The Pernicious Consequences of replacing Denver-Dam and Sluices.* 1745 (B.M.).

Lysons, D. and S. *Cambridgeshire, Magna Britannia.* London, W. Davies, 1808.

Martin, J. P. *Presentation to Joseph Martin Esq., of Littleport, 1909.* (Littleport Fen Office.)

Maxwell, G. *An Essay on Drainage and Navigation occasioned by the Scheme now in agitation for improving the Outfall of the River Ouse.* 1792 (Fen Tracts, C.C.R.O.).
See Board of Agriculture.

Miller, S. H. *The Handbook to the Fenland.* Simpkin and Marshall, 1889.

Mottram, R. H. with Coote, C. *Through Five Generations, a history of the Butterley Company.* London, Faber, 1950.

Mylne, R. *Report of Robert Mylne on the Proposed Improvement of the Drainage and Navigation of the River Ouse.* 1792 (B.M.).
Robert Mylne, Architect and Engineer, 1733–1811 by A. E. Richardson. Batsford, London, 1955.

Neale, T. *The Ruinous State of the parish of Manea, in the Isle of Ely, with the causes and remedy of it humbly presented in a letter to Matt. Robinson Morris Esq., Lord of the Manor of Coveney with Manea.* 1748 (B.M.).

Nickalls, J. *Report upon the Consequences which the New Cut, from Eau-Brink would be attended with to the Drainage, Navigation, the Harbour and Town of Lynn.* 1793 (Fen Tracts, C.C.R.O.).

Parkin, C. *The Topography of Freebridge Hundred and Half in the County of Norfolk.* 1762 (B.M.).

Parkinson, R. *See* Board of Agriculture.

Priestley, J. *An Historical Account of the Navigable Rivers, Canals and Railways throughout Great Britain.* London, Longmans, 1831.

Pusey, P. "Some account of the Practise of English Farmers in the Improvement of Peaty Ground", *J.R.A.S.*, vol. 2, 1841.

"On the Agricultural Improvements of Lincolnshire", *J.R.A.S.*, vol. 4, 1843.

Rennie, J. *Report of Messrs. Jessop, Rennie, Maxwell and Hare on Deeping Fen.* 1800 (L.C.R.O.).

Report and Estimate on the Improvement of the Drainage and Navigation of the South and Middle Levels of the Great Level of the Fens, 24 May 1809 (C.U.L.).

Reports as to the Wisbech Outfall and the Drainage of the North Level and South Holland, 26 January 1814 (C.U.L.).

See Boucher, C. T. G.

Rennie, Sir J. *Autobiography of Sir John Rennie.* London, 1875.

Richards, W. *The History of Lynn.* Lynn, W. G. Whittingham, 1812.

Rolt, L. T. C. *Thomas Newcomen, The Prehistory of the Steam Engine.* London, David and Charles, 1963.

Ross, J. *Treatise on Navigation by Steam.* London, 1828.

Smith, H. *Scheme for draining the South and Middle Levels of the Fens.* 1729 (Fen Tracts, C.C.R.O.).

Stokhuyzen, F. *The Dutch Windmill*, London, Merlin Press, 1962.

Stone, T. *See* Board of Agriculture.

Stuart, R. *Descriptive History of the Steam Engine.* London, Knight and Lacey, 1828.

Telford, T. *Life of Thomas Telford, written by himself.* London, 1838.

Thirsk, J. *English Peasant Farming.* London, 1957.

Tregold, T. *The Steam Engine.* London, 1827.

Triewald, M. *Short Description of the Atmospheric Engine*, 1734. Translated by the Newcomen Society as Extra Publication, no. 1, 1928.

Vancouver, C. *See* Board of Agriculture.

Wailes, R. "The Windmills of Cambridgeshire", *Newcomen Transactions*, 1950.

Walker, N., and Craddock, T. *The History of Wisbech and the Fens.* Wisbech, R. Walker, 1849.

Warburton, E. *Life of Horace Walpole.* London, 1851.

Watson, W. *An Historical Account of the Ancient Town and Port of Wisbech.* Wisbech, 1827.

Watt, J. *Technical Inventions of James Watt.* London, W. Clowes and Sons, 1854.

Wells, S. *The History of the Drainage of the Great Level of the Fens, called Bedford Level.* London, R. Pheney, 1830.

Wheeler, W. H. *The History of the Fens of South Lincolnshire.* London, Simpkin and Marshall, 1868.

Report on the Improvement of the River Ouse between Denver Sluice and the Eau Brink Cut. 1884.

The Drainage of Fens and Low Lands by Gravitation and Steam Power. 1888.

The History of the Fens of South Lincolnshire. 2nd ed. much enlarged, Boston, Newcombe, 1897.

White, H. "A detailed Report of the Drainage by Steam-Power of a Portion of Martin Mere, Lancashire", *J.R.A.S.*, vol. 14, 1853.

Wing, T. *Considerations on the Principles of Mr. Rennie's Plans for the Drainage of the North Level, South Holland etc., with a view to their practical adoption.* 1820 (B.M.).

Young, A. *Annals of Agriculture.*

See Board of Agriculture.

The Index

Figs in italic refer to Illustrations, etc.